SO YOU WANT
TO BE A SCIENTIST

Other Books by Alan E. Nourse

So You Want to Be a Doctor

So You Want to Be a Lawyer
(with William B. Nourse)

So You Want to

Be a Scientist

by ALAN E. NOURSE, M.D.

HARPER & ROW, PUBLISHERS
New York, Evanston, and London

For BEN

CONTENTS

CONTENTS

INTRODUCTION

THIS BOOK IS written for the many young men and women who have become interested in science and in the life and work of scientists.

Every year thousands of you are graduating from high schools all over the country and are taking your first steps in the direction of scientific training. There are more of you now than there used to be; in recent years especially you have been urged and encouraged on all sides to think seriously of careers in science. As a result, many of you who might never have considered it before are now wondering if scientific work of some sort might not be the thing for you to do. It is my hope that this book may help to lead you to an intelligent decision.

With some of you, of course, there is no decision to be made. You have already firmly decided that you want to be a scientist; possibly you have even chosen the particular field of science in which you want to work. Even though you may not be entirely certain just what science is or what you must do to become a scientist, you are starting off with some kind of clear-cut goal in mind. The sheer momentum of your interest and enthusiasm will carry you over many of the rough spots, and very probably you would find your way into a career in science without the help of any guidebooks. But you sense that the road you are following may be very difficult, and you suspect that a better understanding of your goal from the first may make the process of getting there a little easier.

Others of you may not have quite such definite goals in mind. Perhaps you are fairly certain that you want to do some sort of scientific work but don't quite know which way to start. You have always been interested in science and found your high school courses in math and chemistry and biology especially interesting. You have enjoyed reading about the lives and work of some of the great scientists of our time and of earlier times. You realize that in some way science—whatever "science" is—has become an enormously important part of our everyday lives, and that somehow the scientists—whatever they may be—seem to play an important role in molding the way we live. You may never have asked yourself just what science is or what scientists really do, yet somewhere in your mind a chord of interest and excitement has been struck. You would like to explore the world of science a little more, at least, to see if you really like it or not.

Still more of you may have only the faintest stirrings of interest in science. Perhaps you are wondering what it would be like to be working in some scientific field. It seems to be the popular thing these days, yet the road you would have to follow looks difficult and long, without very many signposts. You would like to know more about what lies ahead before deciding whether you are really interested or not.

But no matter where you may stand in these groups, a good road map would be extremely helpful. This, then, is a book about science and about scientists and what they do. It is written as a guidebook for those of you who are interested

in careers in science but would like to know more about the
work and the life you are contemplating before you finally
make a decision. Almost any kind of scientific career will
require you to have a minimum of four years of college
education and training, and many of you will go on to earn
advanced degrees requiring more years of training. Even
the minimum of four years in college will mean a significant
investment of time and money; it would be wise to have as
clear a picture as possible of the goal you are seeking before you undertake such an investment.

This book will not answer all of your questions about
science and scientific training, by any means. There are
literally hundreds of different fields of scientific work; I
will not attempt even to list all of them here, much less go
into great detail about any one of them. Instead, I will try to
present a clear basic picture of what a career in science is
like and outline the general directions that your training
in science will take, no matter what field you ultimately
choose. With this kind of "base-line" understanding of the
scientist's work and training as a background, the details
come readily into focus and make sense; without it they
are merely confusing.

Thus, the first section of the book will explore the life of
the scientist in general and the sort of work he does. Even if
you are already intent upon a career as a pituitary os-
moreceptorologist and nothing else, it will still be helpful
first to have a clear idea of what a *scientist* is, and a picture
in your mind of the whole world of science and what it is
attempting to achieve.

Another part of the book will be devoted to a general
survey of scientific education. How does a scientist get to be
a scientist? What special qualifications of intelligence, interest, or personality are likely to be most helpful to him?

What will his training in science be like? How can he tell as
he goes along just how far he ought to travel on the road to
science, and when he would be wise to stop?

Further on in the book we will discuss in more detail some
of the broad fields of science and the differences between
them. The individual who hopes to become a nuclear physicist will be faced with different problems from the one who
is interested in one of the life sciences such as genetics. By
considering some of the similarities and differences that
exist between the great classifications of science, the book
will provide some guideposts to help in selecting a place in a
vast, exciting field of work.

Finally, we will look briefly at a few of the great scientific
frontiers of the future—fields of knowledge, barely glimpsed
as yet, which will be waiting to challenge the young scientists
who are just now beginning their training.

There is obviously not room enough in a single small
book to say everything there is to be said about science and
scientific education. In order to avoid confusion, I have set
certain arbitrary limits on what I want to discuss here and
what I will purposely leave out. Those of you who are
gadget-minded will notice that I have very little to say
about engineering in this book. There are certain fundamental differences between science, technology, and engineering, even though the dividing lines are often almost
impossible to see. For purposes of clarity I will make a sharp
distinction between science—the creative work of gathering
knowledge—and engineering—the executive work of finding
ways to use that knowledge once it is acquired.

Anyone who enters into scientific work soon becomes
aware of a similar distinction between "pure" science and
"applied" science. In this case, I will try to make the dis-

tinction clear throughout the book but will arbitrarily direct what I have to say mostly toward training and work in pure science.

Again, there are those who will argue vehemently that mathematics is not a science at all, while others will argue just as vigorously that mathematics is the *only* true science. Following my own convictions, I will take a middle ground and discuss mathematics as a basic and integral part of any scientific discipline as well as a science in its own right.

It is emphatically *not* my intention in this book to try to "sell" anyone on the idea of entering a career in science, or to paint an overly colorful picture of the excitement and opportunity that can be found here. Far better salesmen than I are doing that job already, perhaps too well. If I can simply show more clearly what scientific work is really like, with its drawbacks and dullnesses as well as its advantages and excitements, and if I can convey a true idea of the rewards and satisfactions that careers in science hold forth for those of you who seek them out, this book will have fulfilled its purpose.

ALAN E. NOURSE, M.D.

North Bend, Washington

SO YOU WANT
TO BE A SCIENTIST

ONE

What Is a Scientist?

IT IS LONG after midnight on a cold December night, but Professor Rutherford is still at work in the gloomy laboratory in the basement of his secluded manor house.

For over a week now the Professor has been working here behind locked doors without even stopping for sleep. He has refused to see all visitors and has ordered the telephone disconnected to prevent any interruption of his concentration. Strange sounds and smells have been emanating from behind these laboratory doors; when his frightened servants have brought the Professor sandwiches at the odd hours he has rung for them, they have glimpsed a room filled with coiled glassware and bubbling retorts, and the Professor himself has peered out at them suspiciously through his thick-lensed glasses as he takes the food, muttering to himself and returning at once to his work again.

But at last the Great Experiment is completed. The laboratory doors burst open and the Professor rushes out, clutching a flask of murky fluid in one hand and a sheaf of cryptic notes in the other. He holds the flask up to the light, his eyes gleaming feverishly, and cries, "I have it! At last I have it!"

The reader can take the story from there. We hardly need mention the Professor's beautiful daughter who has been worrying about his health during this time of trial, or the cages filled with experimental animals in the back of the laboratory, or the professor's venial and ambitious laboratory assistant, who is plotting to marry the daughter and steal the Professor's secret formula as soon as it is perfected. These members of the supporting cast are so familiar that we just take them for granted. And it goes without saying that the secret formula, whatever it may be, is of earth-shaking importance, a boon to mankind if used properly, but an unspeakable plague if it falls into evil hands. . . .

We all know the picture I have described above by heart; we have seen it presented a thousand times over in motion pictures, on the television screen, or in countless popular stories and novels. It is called forth any time we think about scientists, and leaps unbidden into our mind whenever such magic words as "laboratory" or "experiment" are mentioned.

But is this picture even remotely suggestive of the true picture of the scientist and the work that he does?

Of course it is not.

It seems that somehow, at one time or another in the past, the scientist got off to a bad start in the public eye. Probably there is no one else in the world who has been so continuously harried and afflicted by the false ideas, half-truths, and misconceptions about him and his work as the modern scientist. In recent years the ridiculous stereotype described above has been modified a bit. The scientist is often young and handsome nowadays and wears a long white lab coat; instead of burrowing in a secret basement laboratory, he is found expounding his theories to charming unmarried lab assistants and scribbling mathematical formulas on the blackboard. Often he appears not as the villain of the story but as the romantic hero, peering through his microscope and saving humanity. But the true nature of the scientist and his work remains cloaked in obscurity as far as the general public is concerned, and he is still commonly assumed to be intellectually brilliant, socially impossible, and at least slightly mad.

The fact that the modern scientist is not necessarily any of these things does not seem to alter the popular picture very much. Not long ago a noted anthropologist and social scientist conducted a survey among American high school students in order to see what impression they had of science and scientists. The picture that was developed was just short of horrifying, particularly to the poor unsuspecting scientist. He saw his work described as dull, laborious, dangerous, or cruel. He saw himself pictured as a cold, precise, and machinelike creature, uninterested in anything but his work, brilliant but mentally unbalanced, an individual apart in almost every way from the accepted way of life, uninterested in friends or family—in fact, almost anything but a normal, friendly human being with the same kind of goals, hopes, and ambitions as anyone else.

But in recent years this popular conception of the scientist has placed us in an uncomfortable and puzzling position. Since the beginning of the Sputnik era people have begun to realize, with a certain amount of shock, that we badly need these scientists. In recent months the magazines and newspapers have published statements by responsible and world-renowned leaders claiming that the future of our country, and even of the human race on earth, depends upon encouraging thousands of our young people to become interested in science and to enter careers in scientific work. Already many who are graduating from high school and starting college have begun to feel this pressure encouraging them into scientific pursuits.

But the unattractive and ridiculous popular picture of the

scientist and what he does has proven a trifle embarrassing. Too many potential scientists are discouraged from the first by the stereotyped picture of the scientist; they assume that this picture must be true, since it is so commonly accepted, and they want no part of it. Others who try to see beyond the stereotype and find out what science and scientists are *really* like find themselves facing a welter of conflicting ideas, half-truths, and arguments that are difficult to believe.

Many of you who have become interested in science for one reason or another already have begun to suspect that the popular stereotype picture of the scientist isn't really true at all. You suspect that the scientist may possibly be a human being after all. Perhaps you know of a scientist who is a friend of the family, who seems to be a fairly normal, likable individual even though you do not quite understand just what he does every day when he goes to work. It may even be that you have inadvertently discovered for yourself some of the wonder and excitement in one field of science or another, and cannot believe that the stereotype picture could be true.

Yet you hesitate to commit yourself to a career in such work; what you have seen yourself doesn't seem to jibe with the things you have heard and seen about science and scientists. Possibly you have become thoroughly confused with the many different branches of science that seem to exist; you can't understand how one can possibly be related to another, and you wonder if there could be some branch of science in which you could find your place without having to be a genius, or slightly mad, in order to succeed.

It is no accident that this bizarre picture of science and scientists has come about. False as the ideas may be, there are a number of perfectly good reasons why they developed and why they still persist in the public mind. But there are

also some very sound reasons why these false ideas should
be exposed to the light, and true ideas of science and the
scientist presented to replace the old. Like it or not, it is a
fact that the scientist and science are playing an increasingly important role in the world we live in. We can no longer
get along just putting up with scientists, like unwelcome
company that won't go home. We are going to have to understand them and encourage them. Certainly anyone who feels
even vague stirrings of interest in some scientific pursuit
would be wise to try to plow through the confusion and
misinformation and develop in his mind a sound picture of
what science is and what the scientist does.

What is a scientist? Obviously, a scientist is an individual
who works in some branch of science. But such an answer is
not very helpful. What then is science, and what are these
"branches" that it is divided up into? What is a scientist
like and what does he do with his time? Are all scientists the
same, or is the scientist in one field different from the scientist in another? What is it that sets him apart from salesmen, lawyers, politicians, teachers, laborers, or any other kind
of worker? Even the dictionary definition of a scientist as
"one learned in science, especially natural science, a scientific investigator," is not a very good answer to the question.

In fact, we will not find out what a scientist is by looking
for a simple definition. The more we think about the question, the more difficult it seems to find a simple and ready
answer. But obviously the scientist is *somebody* and he does
something. There must be some way to develop a clear picture
of just what he is and what sort of work he does.

The Scientists in Our Life

On the third floor of a laboratory building in a Pacific
Coast medical school, a young man in a white lab coat is

busily pouring a fluid from a beaker into a series of small
cotton-stoppered flasks. The little room where he is working
is a combination of laboratory, coat room and office; it is
small, rather dark, and not too clean. Against one wall a
row of book shelves are filled to overflowing with textbooks,
scientific journals, and piles of manuscript. On the laboratory bench are a microscope and several large glass-fronted
incubators. The incubators are filled with flasks of broth,
and today this young man is engaged in the rather tedious
job of transferring a few drops of a suspension of living
cells into each of some three hundred and fifty flasks.

One might assume that the worried look on this young
man's face reflects his concern that the inoculations be accomplished without error. Actually, he is worried more about
how long it will take him to finish the job. The cultures
must all be planted today, but he was twice interrupted
this afternoon by unexpected visitors to the laboratory. At
seven o'clock he and his wife are expecting another couple
for dinner, and he is wondering if he will get home with
time enough to shave and shower before the guests arrive.

This young man is a doctor of philosophy in the field
of genetics. He works at the medical school and even lectures
to the medical students for two hours every week, but his
salary is paid by a federal government grant. The work
that he is doing was originally planned to take two or three
years; now he suspects that it may take five, and he worries
considerably whether his grant money will be renewed. He
is engaged in a quest for information about the behavior
of a certain chemical compound known as desoxyribose nucleic
acid, one of a number of substances found in the chromosomes
of all living cells. This substance has long been suspected
of exerting a great influence on the way those cells grow
and reproduce and develop; by studying the way it behaves

in living cells under a series of rigidly controlled special conditions, this young man hopes to learn more about its function and perhaps to discover the way it influences the physical characteristics of new cells.

This kind of work involves many different types of activities. Part of this young man's time is spent in his laboratory, and part in the library. Much of his time, whether "at work" or not, is spent just mulling over the complexities of the problems facing him. He does not think of himself as particularly different from his banker or his garage mechanic or his doctor friend, or from the salesman who comes to his office periodically to check up on his supplies. The tools of his work are simple: a few standard pieces of glassware, an incubator-type oven, a microscope, a scratch pad, and a considerable store of knowledge he has accumulated about genetics, living cells, genes, and chromosomes. He has difficulty telling his non-scientist friends just exactly what he is trying to accomplish with his work simply because there are not more than a dozen people in the country who know enough about his special field of genetics to understand him— yet if he finds some unsuspecting fellow who is willing to listen, he will eagerly talk about his work until somebody comes to turn him off.

He is a geneticist, but first he is a scientist. . . .

In another part of the country a young woman is working in a large, well-equipped laboratory in a beautiful building lying outside the city. This young woman has a bachelor's degree in chemistry, with a minor in biology. She is employed by one of the large drug-manufacturing houses, working on the research team searching for new medications for the company to produce. For the past two years she and some fifty other scientists have been busy separating and screening over fifty thousand varieties of soil bacteria in search of one which may produce a new and useful antibiotic drug. About three dozen varieties were found to produce enough antibacterial substance to be worth studying, and three of these look really promising.

Now this young woman is busy testing these antibiotic substances to determine dangerous or toxic side effects they may have in living creatures. Others on the team are studying their chemical structure, and trying to synthesize them in the laboratory. Still others are trying to alter them artificially, in hopes of developing more antibiotic effect with fewer poisonous side effects.

This woman is paid a salary by her employer. The project she is working on is not her own idea; she was assigned to work on it, and she has been using her scientific knowledge to help achieve a predetermined goal: the development of a useful, effective, safe antibiotic which her company can then produce and sell. As a salaried employee working on somebody else's idea along lines that have been set out for her, she is typical of thousands of applied scientists in industry today. But first and foremost, she is a scientist. . . .

In a city in the Middle West an orthopedic surgeon greets a patient in his office and then eagerly waits for the most recent X-rays of the patient's previously broken leg to be developed by his X-ray technician. This patient is of special interest to the surgeon. The fracture was of a type which has always been notoriously difficult to set and keep in the proper position for healing. For some years this surgeon, busy in his office and in the operating room, has been thinking about a new technique for setting this kind of a fracture; when this patient was first brought to his office, he obtained the patient's permission to attempt a new method of treatment which he felt would be superior to any other.

And now, when he sees the films, he is pleased and excited. The bone has healed perfectly in a third less time than normally would be expected. This is the first in a series of forty such patients whom the surgeon has been watching. When he has the results of all forty fractures in hand, he will gather them together and publish his method of treatment in the *American Journal of Orthopedic Surgery*. He knows that if the results of these forty cases are promising, orthopedic surgeons all over the country will try this method, and possibly another step forward will have been taken in the treatment of difficult fractures.

This man is a physician, a surgeon with a busy practice and a happy home life, but he is also a scientist. . . .

In a pleasant section of suburban Philadelphia, a soft-spoken man with horn-rimmed glasses walks into the concrete building which he smilingly calls his "tool shop" to conduct another step in an experiment which has been occupying him for some four years. The main "tool" in this man's tool shop is a machine that stands in a shaft three stories high and cost millions of dollars to build. It is a Van De Graff generator, a type of atom-smasher capable of developing several billion electron-volts of energy. Ironically, the object of this man's search, for which he needs this Gargantuan tool, is a particle of matter so tiny that it will never be seen, and so difficult to identify that it took years of experimenting to be certain that it even existed.

This man is a nuclear physicist. He uses his huge generator in many ways to study the changes that occur in the nuclei of atoms. But he is mainly interested in one tiny particle of matter known as a "meson." If his work succeeds, he will have established one more bit of knowledge about the basic structure of all the matter that makes up our universe. The an-

swers he is seeking could profoundly influence the thinking
of physicists, mathematicians, astronomers, and a host of
other people in a dozen different scientific fields. In a way, he
is a craftsman, using a highly specialized tool for a highly
specialized purpose, but above all else he is a scientist. . . .

In an office in Washington, D.C., another scientist sits
working late into the night. The tools of his trade are different
from the physicist's; he uses only a thick yellow scratch pad
which he bought at the dime store, and three soft-lead pencils.
Forty or fifty other people work with him in this office during
the day, but this young man has long since learned that he
can concentrate better when the noise and confusion of the
workday are over, so lately he has been coming back after
dinner to work by himself until midnight. For eighteen
months he has been trying to translate a complex problem
into the kind of language that an electronic computer can
understand. This is a difficult problem in mathematics, and
the young man is a mathematician. For months he fumbled
his way up blind alleys, carrying out lines of mathematical
reasoning to fruitless ends. Only recently has he found a line
of approach which looks fruitful, and he now feels confident
that within three or four more months of full-time work he
should have the answer under control.

Of course, he realizes that by the time he has the problem
solved, the particular computing machine with which he has
been working will already be obsolete and the work he has
been doing for eighteen months will never actually be used.
Other people might be discouraged by this knowledge; it does
not disturb our young friend one bit. He has enjoyed the
challenge of digging out the solution to a difficult problem
that has never before been solved, and he knows that methods
he has discovered for solving this problem will greatly speed
up the programming of any future computer problem.

He is a mathematician who works with a pad and pencil and a clutter of symbols which make no sense to most of his friends. He leads a lonely life too; the work he is doing is considered top secret by the government. He cannot even discuss it with other mathematicians, and his notes and calculations are either filed under lock and key or carried under armed guard to the incinerators to be burned. But these facts to him are minor annoyances; the work he is doing is immensely exciting and satisfying, and this is to be expected because this young man is a scientist. . . .

It is a hot summer night and the dark sky is peppered with bright pinpoints of stars. High in the loft of one of his father's farm outbuildings, a high school sophomore has been working for several hours to focus a small homemade reflector telescope on a particular section of the heavens that he is interested in. There is nothing particularly odd about this young man. Every morning he waits for the bus that takes him in to school in the neighboring town. His grades could be better, and he had to argue long and eloquently for his parents' permission to stay up beyond ten o'clock on a school night. He has spent some fifty dollars of his own paper-route money for the lenses and materials to go into the telescope he has made, but it has proven to be a good, workable instrument. Using it earlier in the summer, he was able to see the rings of Saturn, and he picked out four of the twelve moons of Jupiter one night, when he finally managed to locate Jupiter.

This particular evening he has another project on his mind. For several nights he has been trying in vain to see the satellite rocket carrier which has been crossing overhead every night. Unable to spot it even with the help of his telescope, he reasoned that it might be spotted with the aid of a camera, and built a special pin-hole camera loaded with highly sensitive film to attach to the telescope. During a ten-minute exposure he knew that the stars would make only pinpoints of light on the camera plate. But if the telescope were aimed in the proper direction, it seemed to him that the rocket carrier ought to make a long, slender streak of light across the plate.

He aims the camera and the telescope in the exact direction the carrier is supposed to cross, exposes it at the proper time, and then rushes the film down into the developing tank he has waiting below. Two weeks of planning, work, and preparation lie behind this experiment, and it is a dreadful disappointment when he develops the film and finds no sign of the anticipated telltale streak of the rocket carrier.

If this young man had had a little more background knowledge, he would have realized that his technique was all right but that his tools were too crude. He would have known that the light reflected from the rocket carrier would be too feeble to compete with the glaring light from the stars themselves, that his plate with the fast, coarse-grained film would be fogged out by the light of the stars. Because of the failure of his experiment he may come to the false conclusion that the rocket carrier never did cross that night, but more likely he will merely spend several nights scratching his head and trying to figure out why his plan didn't work, and then set out to try another technique to make it work the next time.

Sooner or later this young man will develop the knowledge he needs and obtain tools of greater refinement to work with. This does not matter to him now. All that matters is that he has discovered a hobby of enormous excitement and fascination. The disappointment of his failure many retire him from the loft for a few nights, but presently he will be back trying the same thing again in a different way. This young man is still a high school student, active on the track team, popular with his friends, vice-president of his class, and about average in his school work. He would probably laugh at the idea if anybody suggested it, but already this young man is a scientist. . . .

The Common Denominators

It might seem at first that these imaginary sketches of scientists at work only add confusion when we try to pin down just what a scientist is. Here we have seen half a dozen people, each one quite different from the others, engaged in a wide variety of pursuits. What can these people possibly have in common? One uses little more than pad and pencil as tools of his trade; another is helpless without a multimillion dollar machine with which to smash atomic nuclei to flinders. One is employed by a large company, punching a time clock and earning a specified salary. Another is practicing medicine, seeing patients and treating illness every day in the hospital and in his office. Still another thinks of his scientific pursuits as nothing more than an exciting hobby, a game that he plays just for fun.

If each of these people is a scientist, then it is hardly any wonder that we get confused when we try to answer the question, "What is a scientist?"

Yet if we look at these people in their variety of different pursuits, we can find certain common denominators. A number of things tend to draw these people together into a group and set them apart from salesmen, or merchants, or lawyers, or people in other nonscientific pursuits.

First of all, we notice that all of these people are engaged in *observing* something. The geneticist is observing the behavior of tissue cells under certain special conditions which he has arranged. The physicist, somewhat paradoxically, is "observing" something which neither he nor anyone else can see, yet which unquestionably exists as one of the basic building-stones of our physical universe. The high school sophomore is observing many things with his telescope in addition to the satellite rocket carrier which he has not succeeded in seeing. Even the mathematician is observing the manner in which certain mathematical ideas either fit or do not fit into the programming problem upon which he is working.

In each case these people are observing some kind of natural phenomenon. Each of them is studying certain natural laws in action, whether it be the laws governing the reaction of chemical substances or the laws controlling the behavior of electronic circuits under certain types of stimuli.

But more is involved in each of these people's work than merely observing something. We could very easily watch something happen a thousand times end-running without understanding either what was happening or why. Men watched the movements of the stars in the sky for thousands of years before they finally discovered what those movements meant and why they occurred the way they did. In addition to observing something, all of these people also have a certain amount of background knowledge gathered from one source or another which helps to make sense out of the phenomena which they are observing. All of them have at one time or another learned a method of *testing* this background knowledge to make sure that it is indeed factual and not merely somebody's guesswork. Next, all of them have made certain guesses on the basis of the background knowledge they have and the things they have observed. All are engaged in speculating or *theorizing*. In a way, each of them is saying, "If *this* is really so, and if I do *this*, *this* ought to be the result."

Finally, all of these people have devised ways to test the guesses they have made, to see whether they are right or not, and all of them have drawn certain *conclusions* from the results of these experiments. These conclusions have then become part of the background knowledge they have.

If we look once again at the dictionary definition of a scientist, we see that there are certain key words which are helpful. The dictionary says that a scientist is "one learned in science, especially natural science; a scientific investigator." In that definition, two words are keys: the word *learned* and the word *investigator*.

Each of the scientists we have described has accumulated an organized body of knowledge about some aspect of the world of nature. The chemist has learned that certain substances join together to form new substances reliably and constantly whenever the right conditions prevail. The physicist has learned that matter is composed of certain basic building blocks which always seem to have certain basic properties. With this background knowledge, each of them has set out to investigate further some phase of the world of nature, to learn more about it, and to understand better how things work and why. Every scientist must be *learned* in some degree in order to know a certain amount that has already been discovered; and every scientist is basically an *investigator*, seeking to learn more about some phase of the world we live in and why it behaves the way it does.

And every scientist in his work uses a peculiar and time-tested method of investigation. There is nothing in the least mysterious about this method. On the contrary, it is so simple and logical that it has become part of the life and thinking of virtually everyone. This way of investigating unknown things and of testing the results and answers of such investigation is known throughout the world as *the scientific method*.

Basically, then, the scientist is nothing more than an intelligent investigator of nature. He may be doing this kind of work for any one of a hundred different reasons. He may do it because he has a burning interest in a certain natural phenomenon and hopes that by learning more about it he can make an important contribution to the world's knowledge. He may do it because he has discovered that he is particularly good at this kind of investigation work, or because someone will pay him a steady (if not particularly handsome) salary for doing it. Or, like the high school astronomer, he may do it simply because he has stumbled into the excitement of the world of nature almost by accident and has discovered that this kind of search for knowledge can be fun.

And by the same token, anyone who finds himself excited and fascinated by the ways that nature works and wants to learn more about it already has the basic equipment he needs to be become a scientist.

The Care and Feeding of Mad Scientists

But if all this is true about the scientist, it would seem at least possible that he might be a fairly normal, sane, rational human being, in contrast to the popular picture of a silent, mysterious, abnormal, and mentally unbalanced fanatic. How then did this widespread misconception of the scientist come about? Surely there must be *some* basis for such ideas. Could there be some truth in these notions even if they are not the whole truth? If they are entirely false, why are they so widely believed?

As a matter of fact, there *is* a kernel of truth in the popular misconception of the scientist—but only a kernel. The daily life of the scientist and his position in society may seem perfectly innocent; we may observe that he has a wife and family, that he maintains a pleasant suburban home, drives an ordinary automobile, starts off to work in the morning and comes home at night, and goes fishing on Saturdays, like anybody else. Yet there are reasons for the distorted picture of the scientist which has grown up. Some of these are extrinsic; they arise from the kind of work the scientist is doing, regardless of the sort of person he may be. Others of the reasons are related to the scientist himself; they are part and parcel of the personality of the kind of person who ultimately ends up becoming a scientist.

Perhaps the major of these reasons is the fact that most scientists are individualists. They do not become individualists just because they are scientists; rather, they tend to become scientists because they are individualists in the first place.

Scientists make their living by and large by thinking. An individual need not necessarily be a genius-type thinker nor even particularly brilliant to be a good scientist, but to gain any degree of success in his work he must be a dogged, persistent, stubborn, single-minded, and never-say-die type of thinker. He must be able to think for himself, without crutches or assistance. He must know how to distinguish between facts on the one hand, and guesses or opinions on the other. Such a person cannot help but be an individualist, doing his own thinking, forming his own opinions and clinging to them whether they happen to agree with other people's opinions or not.

What is more, the central goal of any kind of scientific training is to teach the individual a particular type and quality of productive thinking. A good scientist must have the ability and the discipline to control his thinking rigidly, to make it do exactly what he wants it to do. He must be capable of pursuing any objective on which he sets his sights with an almost fanatical intensity. The habit of thinking-with-a-purpose—questioning, probing, revising the questions, and requestioning—must become a built-in part of the scientist's personality. If he did not have this capability he would never have survived the long grind of scientific education.

I am not by any means contending that nonscientific people don't think; I am merely suggesting that they don't spend as much time thinking, nor do they necessarily think in the same ways or toward the same goals as the scientist does.

The scientist must continuously apply his ingrained habits of disciplined thinking to his work. Quite naturally, he tends to carry these habits over into other parts of his life. If his ideas about politics, foreign policy, or the rearing of children do not conform to the ideas of the people around him, he is not disturbed in the least (although the ones with whom he disagrees are often immensely disturbed!). Since it is the nature of his work to seek out evidence to support his ideas and opinions, the scientist is often an extremely difficult individual to argue with, no matter how upsetting or nonconforming his ideas may be. Right or wrong, he is very likely to have logical reasons for his views and will stubbornly refuse to buckle under to the opinions of others just because they feel that he ought to.

It is precisely this sort of intellectual independence and stubbornness, absolutely necessary in the performance of sound scientific investigation, which so often makes the scientist an awkward and uncomfortable fellow to have around. Other aspects of his work only add to this awkwardness. The scientist's thinking often leads him to uncomfortable or unpleasant conclusions in his work. He frequently must face the fact that he may have been dead wrong about something from the start. He must be ready at any time to revise his thinking completely, to throw out a whole series of pet ideas and start over again—an experience which most nonscientists are not accustomed to and would find exceedingly difficult and painful.

Again, the scientist can rarely leave his work on his desk at night and pick it up again in the morning. He may work with such equipment as atom-smashers or electronic computers, but these are only tools to help him. Ninety-five per cent of the important part of the scientist's work is actually being done somewhere in the region above his ears. He has a perplexing problem to solve and he is almost continuously at work trying to solve it. At the end of a day he may come home to his family; he may take his son on a weekend fishing trip, or go dancing with his wife, or go out to a movie, or spend an evening arguing politics with his neighbor, but all the time some part of his mind is busily chipping away at his problem. This sort of continuous, unrelieved preoccupation with a problem at hand is often very puzzling to the nonscientist; why won't the fellow just forget it for a while? The fact is that usually he just plain can't forget it for a while, even if he wants to. Until the problem is solved, he is stuck with it, like it or not. If he could switch it on and off at will, chances are he would never have become a scientist in the first place!

So far we have been talking about intrinsic reasons for the distorted popular picture of scientists, personality traits that the scientist can't really do very much about. But there are extrinsic reasons, too—problems that are forced down the scientist's throat from the outside, so to speak, with which he must cope as best he can. And trouble with communications is probably the greatest of these problems.

One of the reasons that the scientist is the object of so much suspicion and so many false ideas about himself and his work is simply a matter of lack of understanding. People distrust what they don't understand, and the scientist has enormous difficulty getting across to nonscientists just exactly what he is doing in his work.

This is not because the scientist doesn't want to talk about his work—try to stop him once he gets started!—or because he has any secret to keep, or because he is engaged in a conspiracy against society, or because he is looking down his nose at nonscientific people as inferiors. It is simply because he has run up against the twin barriers of *knowledge* and *language*. All too often these barriers seem insurmountable in talking with nonscientific people.

Whatever work the scientist may be doing, he has behind him a huge fund of specialized background knowledge. There is nothing particularly mysterious about this knowledge or the way he has acquired it. After all, the butcher has a specialized knowledge of briskets and loin chops which the average layman doesn't have and which is enough to confuse the most intelligent housewife when she goes shopping for her Sunday roast. If the scientist wants to talk about the work that he is doing, why he is doing it, and what it will mean when he is finished, he first must be able to explain enough of his background knowledge to his audience to make some kind of sense. And this is so difficult to do that very few scientists have the patience, or even the ability, to do it.

The barrier of language is even more difficult. Because it it easier and speeds up his work, the scientist in any field uses a special type of jargon in describing what he is doing. He uses units of measurement which are not in common everyday use. He uses descriptive terms which convey a great deal of accurate information quickly to those who are acquainted with the terms, but which sound like hocus-pocus to the uninitiated. When a doctor reports that a patient has acute coronary insufficiency with secondary myocardial ischemia and T-wave changes consistent with a recent posterior-lateral infarction, any doctor in the country will know exactly what he means; if he tells the patient the same thing, the patient says, "That's fine, Doctor, but what's giving me this pain in the chest?" The doctor may be able to translate the diagnosis into terms the patient can understand, but it may take him a half an hour to do it.

Contrary to popular suspicions, scientists do not use scientific jargon for the purpose of confusing nonscientists or of hiding their work from the public eye. The jargon is a form of verbal shorthand, an invaluable time and work saver. But there aren't many scientists with either the patience or the command of the English language necessary to convey quickly and easily to nonscientists what the jargon means, and most of those who try soon discover that there are few nonscientists who are really interested enough to listen and find out. It is much easier just to assume that the scientist's work is mysterious and obscure, that he uses jargon purposely because he is "secretive" and doesn't really want to tell you what he is doing, or because he is poking fun at your stupidity.

Finally, there is an even more general reason why scientists have been viewed with so much suspicion in recent years. Even accepting their inability to tell people what they are doing or how they are doing it, and ignoring their continuous preoccupation with their work whether they are in the laboratory or not, there still seems to be good reason to be suspicious of these people. How could the scientists possibly be normal, trustworthy individuals when their work results in so many thoroughly unpleasant problems?

We are living in a world where the contributions of scientists seem to be pressing in on us from every side. The work they have done has changed the food we eat, the homes we live in, the cities we build, and the work we do. We have to admit that scientists have contributed an enormous amount to our daily life and welfare, yet at the same time it seems that they are incessantly opening up Pandora's boxes. Too many of their discoveries have proved to be double-edged weapons. Too often the scientists have been the ones who have raised painful, uncomfortable questions, bringing forth knowledge that has both beneficial and horrible implications.

There could be no better example of this than the work of the scientists on the Manhattan project during World War II. In a few short years of intensive work, these scientists unleashed from the basic structure of the atom an enormous source of power—power enough to improve our lives in a million ways or to wipe life off the face of the earth in one fell swoop. Time and again the scientists have been the uncoverers of awkward and painful truths which, once turned up, have to be faced. The temptation has been great to look for a scapegoat, and it has been very easy indeed, while struggling with the unpleasant contents of these Pandora's boxes, for people to blame the scientists for having lifted the lid in the first place.

Hardships and Rewards

Fortunately, we can expect that in the next few years the popular picture of the scientist will gradually change. The scientist is becoming more and more a critical cog in the machinery of our everyday life. It is increasingly obvious that we need scientists badly if we hope to survive in the modern world. Efforts will surely be made to make the scientist and his life more palatable to the general public; the old attitude of "Throw a stick at him and maybe he'll go away" will at least be replaced with the attitude of "Well, we don't really like him very much, but we'll put up with him if we must."

Nevertheless it seems likely that the scientist will always stand apart from nonscientific people in many ways, and anyone who is considering a career in science will simply have to accept this as one of the minor hardships. In this book perhaps we can make a little more clear a true picture of the scientist's life and point out some of the rewards which accrue to the scientist to make up for the hardships.

There are other hardships a scientist will have to face. In many scientific fields today the scientist must work under an imposed secrecy. Much of the work being done in physics, aerodynamics, chemistry, and mathematics is considered critical to national security, and the scientist working in almost any field may find himself bound to secrecy in his work. This can be a real hardship and impediment, since it limits the exchange of information between scientists, sometimes even between scientists working in the same laboratory on the same program. It can also be a real danger to progress in critical scientific programs. Nothing can be more crippling to scientific work, or more demoralizing to the scientist, than to have needed scientific information withheld or unavailable for entirely nonscientific (and too often irrational) reasons.

Of course anyone involved in such "classified" work must undergo some level of security clearance, and this can be still more of a headache to the scientists. Perhaps because they are engaged in opening Pandora's boxes and other unpopular work, scientists are more vulnerable than other individuals to attack on the basis of their political opinions, their associations with other people, or things they have written or said in the past. Certainly the government has lost the services of many excellent and loyal scientists who have become discouraged or driven away by such impediments thrown in the path of the work they want to do.

Not a hardship, but a problem that everyone entering a scientific career will encounter at one time or another is the conflict between pure science, the free, utterly independent accumulation of scientific knowledge for its own sake, and applied science, the kind of "science with a purpose" that is so widely supported by the government and by industry. We will discuss later just what the differences are between pure and applied science, and just what chances an individual has of finding a place that will be comfortable in one or the other. For now it is enough to say that most scientists, given their choice, would far prefer to work in pure science (or think they would)—but very few can afford it. On the other hand, very few scientists would elect to work in applied science, if all other things were equal—yet most scientists are forced by circumstances to do so and, as we will see, it is probably just as well that they are.

With all this talk of hardships and problems, you may be wondering by now just why anybody goes into a scientific career in the first place. The answer is, of course, that the scientist finds certain rewards in his work that make up a dozen times over for the hardships and annoyances he must put up with. With his basic education and training behind him, a scientist can find a high degree of security in his work. His salary may not be large, but it is likely to be stable and dependable. He may never become rich as a scientist, but chances are good that he will never be hungry either; with the steadily rising demand for his abilities, the scientist with any skill at all will always have a job.

Further, he will have the satisfaction of working in a field where his work is badly needed, and in which he can find an enormous sense of personal achievement. He may never achieve a great breakthrough in his life; very few scientists do. Nevertheless, his contributions to science may pave the way, and every scientist at least has the opportunity to leave his name and his mark in the halls of greatness.

But there is an overwhelming reward which every scientist will find at one time or another which can blot out all of the hardships and compensate for all of the distorted pictures and suspicions and false accusations of his fellowmen: the sheer blinding excitement of discovery, the uncovering of something which was hidden until his work was begun and now is revealed, the unbelievable gratification of tackling a difficult problem and hanging on through months or years of hard, disappointing, difficult work until the answer is in his hands.

This one thing alone, most scientists would agree, will compensate for everything else. There may be a ceiling on the scientist's salary and a ceiling on the position or power he may achieve, but there is no ceiling on what he can accomplish, and no compensation—no matter how great—could substitute for the sheer satisfaction of spending his life doing the kind of work which he would rather do than anything else in the world.

But in order to see how this can be such a compelling reward, we must look beyond the scientist and consider for a moment the world of science in which he works. In order to understand what the scientist does in his work and why he does it, we need a clear understanding of what science is, of the way its many fields are related to each other, and of the important part that it plays in our daily lives.

TWO

The Wonderful World of Science

IF SOMEONE WERE to ask you to describe a house in five hundred words or less, chances are you would not find it too difficult to do.

You might choose any one of several different approaches. Perhaps you would base your description on dimensions and form, looking upon the house as several geometrical units joined together to form an enclosed space. Possibly you would describe it in terms of appearance—sloping roof, straight walls, painted trim, and surrounding greenery. If you were a bit more imaginative, you might start with the function of a house and describe it in terms of its use as a shelter or a home. And the odds are good that at least some of you would reject the whole project as foolishness and refuse to write a description at all. After all, everybody already knows what a house is.

Of course, everybody knows what "happiness" is, too, but defining it clearly and accurately in words can be quite a job. A house is a discrete, solid object we can examine and describe easily, while happiness is an abstract idea, much more difficult to pin down in words.

Everybody knows what "science" is, too, until it comes to the job of defining it. And there we begin to get into trouble.

Hardly a day goes by that we do not hear the word "science" used in one way or another. All of us are aware that something called "science" exists in the world. Whatever it is, it seems to concern a great many very wise people, and it seems to have a great deal of influence on our everyday lives. We read in the papers about "the discoveries of science," about "the progress of science," and "the great advancements of science." We hear of the need for "more science in our schools" and of the importance of science for our national security. We even hear supposedly responsible people talking about "combatting the science" of certain hostile nations, as though it were something that could be shot down out of the sky like a widgeon!

And wherever we turn, whether at home or in school or downtown shopping or out driving, we are surrounded by the products of science: the machines, the fabrics, the foods, the methods of doing things which have become integral parts of our lives.

In the previous chapter we took a brief look at the scientist —the man who practices or works in science—and saw some of the places where the scientist might be found and a few of the kinds of work that he might be doing. But in order to understand the scientist and his work better, we need to know more about the science that he practices. We know science is important to us, we know it is responsible in many ways for the way we live—but what is it? We hear about a thousand different branches or fields of science; how can we make any sense out of the confusion among these branches of science and the kinds of work that they involve?

The Circle of Science

For an incomplete but useful working definition, we can say that *science is the study of the natural laws which govern the universe.*

The universe we live in is filled with activity and change. Subatomic particles or forces join together and interact to form atoms; atoms combine to form molecules or separate to form other atoms and subatomic particles. Molecules form the building blocks of both inanimate matter—the nonliving material of the planet on which we live and the other planetary and stellar bodies—and animate matter—the living cells and creatures which inhabit this planet and perhaps millions of others. The forces that cause these building blocks to act together are always moving, never at rest. Although we can recognize this ceaseless activity of nature most easily in the living creatures around us, it is going on just as constantly in a block of granite as in a living organism.

But this activity of nature which occurs in our universe does not appear to happen by chance. This constant inter-action of matter and energy proceeds according to certain patterns which we call "natural laws." The same kind of activity always seems to happen in the same way under the same circumstances. These natural laws which govern the universe are fixed and unchanging; they can be observed, tested, and identified, if we can only find intelligent ways to observe them, accurate ways to test them, and reliable ways to identify them.

The "science" that we speak of is a unified endeavor to study and understand these natural laws and the way in which they govern the behavior of the universe and every-thing in it.

Some of these natural laws merely explain things that men have long observed but never understood; knowledge of them has no particular usefulness to us other than satisfying our curiosity. Thus, the knowledge that our sun is one of several billion stars in a galaxy which is expanding at an enormous rate of speed may be very interesting, but it doesn't change our daily lives very much. An understanding of other natural laws, however, has shown us ways that they could be put to work for us and used, and the intelligent application of them has completely revolutionized our lives.

Incredible as it may seem, this concept of a universe governed by natural laws is a comparatively new notion. Today we readily accept the idea that the universe is an orderly place in which everything happens for a natural reason and brings about a predictable effect. To us this seems so obvious, so much a part of our thinking that we can hardly believe that only a few centuries ago men had no idea that there were natural laws controlling the world and everything in it. Primitive men thought that things happened by chance and caprice, as a result of the influence of good and evil spirits or according to the whimsy of a group of mythical gods. No one dreamed of trying to learn what made things happen and then using that knowledge to predict other things which might happen. In the primitive world there was no science, no organized study of nature, nor even any great curiosity about it.

Yet even in the Stone Age primitive men had long since learned that it was easier to move a boulder by wedging a stick under it and prying it up than by rolling it out of its hole unaided. They had even learned that the longer and stouter the stick was, the larger the boulder that could be pried up. One of the basic natural laws of physics, the law of the lever and the fulcrum, had already been discovered even though it was not recognized as a natural law. The pyramids of Egypt and the Babylonian Hanging Gardens of ancient times were projects that would have taxed the ingenuity of our best trained scientists and engineers today, yet they were accomplished without even an understanding that natural laws of physics existed.

But bit by bit over the centuries a few men grew impatient with the idea that everything around them happened by chance. Certain things obviously behaved in a consistent, orderly fashion—why not all things? The idea arose that the truth or nontruth of an idea could be demonstrated and

proved, and men began to experiment with their surround-
ings, trying to find ways to be sure just what was true and
what was not. Bit by bit men began to suspect that everything in nature was governed by fixed rules. With the first
attempts to identify those rules, science as we know it was
born.

Of course, like any new and revolutionary idea, the idea of
natural law had more enemies than friends at first. Some men
thought it was immoral and evil to ask questions about why
things happened as they did. Others insisted that this growing
idea of natural laws governing things was opposed to the
teachings of faith of the Christian church, and many early
scientists were persecuted for their studies and forced to deny
in public the facts that they could actually prove were true!

And, indeed, the earliest approaches to the study of natural
laws were anything but scientific. The great philosophers of
Greece were certain that nature could best be investigated by
deep and abstract thought, without cluttering up their minds
with measurements and observations. Investigation by experimentation was fit only for slaves, and the notion of deliberately seeking to apply the laws of nature to the problems of
everyday living drew bitter attacks.

So the investigation of natural laws by means of experimentation had to wait two thousand years to come into its own.
Then—and only then—did science really begin to blossom.

So far, you will notice we have been speaking about all
kinds of natural laws. We have said nothing about different
types and have made no attempt to separate them into categories. Science is concerned with any and all natural phenomena; it seeks to explain any and all of the laws of nature.
Yet from earliest times it was recognized that the whole of
nature was just too much for any one man, or even a group of
men, to try to investigate at one time. The philosophers tried
to take the whole of creation and reduce it to a simple pattern.

The scientist had to be content to study a tiny fragment of the world of nature at a time, in hopes that eventually he could piece together the entire picture. Very early, scientists began to select certain types of natural law to investigate, and the fields or branches of science began to appear.

Thus, among the earliest scientists there were a few who attempted to understand the rising and setting of the sun and the movements of the stars across the heavens. The study of this particular aspect of the natural world became known as astronomy. Another group of men turned their attention to the relationships of lines and angles on a flat plane, and plane geometry became one of the earliest systems of mathematics to be discovered. Still other men began describing and classifying various forms of plant and animal life; they became the first natural scientists. Much later, when experimentation became accepted as a means of studying nature, the experimental fields of chemistry and physics began to grow.

This sort of division of labor among scientists had certain great advantages. It allowed a given scientist to become thoroughly acquainted with a limited field of science; he could then concentrate on ferreting out new knowledge in that field and not have to worry about any of the others. Many fields of science were closely related, but as scientific knowledge grew, the whole spectrum of science seemed to fall into three great categories: the physical sciences, the life sciences, and the earth sciences.

This same division of the world of science into categories is still used today; for convenience we will use it in this book, even though it results in a somewhat distorted picture. Certain fields of science have to do with the physical nature of matter, with atoms and molecules and the way they react together. In this group of *physical sciences* physics and chemistry are dominant. Certain other fields are concerned with the structure of the earth and the nature of the universe beyond the earth. These so-called *earth sciences* include geology and astronomy. Finally, a whole group of scientific fields deal with the nature of living creatures. These *life sciences*, or biological sciences, include botany, zoology, and medicine.

Unfortunately, it is easy to forget that this division of science into neat pigeon-hole categories is a 100 per cent man-made device. The laws of nature themselves are not separated into tidy little groups; rather, they interweave and dovetail, each supplementing and supporting all the others like the pieces in an enormously complicated three-dimensional jig-saw puzzle. It follows that there could not possibly be any rigid dividing lines between the various fields of science. Each one is inseparably related to all of the others.

This is sometimes difficult to see. How could such different fields as chemistry and zoology have anything to do with each other? After all, chemistry deals with individual chemical substances and the ways they react when they are heated or chilled or mixed together in certain ways, while zoology has to do with the way living animals grow, reproduce, and behave. Yet when we look more closely we see that all living creatures are composed of specific chemical substances. We cannot hope to understand how living organisms grow and maintain life without first knowing a great deal about the chemical substances that make them up.

Considered this way, it would be hard to insist that chemistry and zoology are really separate and distinct fields of science with no overlap between the two. We would have even more trouble trying to classify such a field as biochemistry either as chemistry (one of the physical sciences) or biology (one of the life sciences).

Similarly, the physicist in his study of the atomic forces that make up all kinds of matter is working hand in glove with the chemist who studies how the molecules composed of these atomic forces react with one another. The great laws of nature which govern the action and movement of atomic particles are not far removed from the laws of nature which control the movement of the stars and planets, and the physicist and astronomer are both aided by the mathematician who attempts by reasoning to determine the natural laws governing space and time. It is no accident that Albert Einstein, the great scientist who spent his life trying to define the relationships among matter, energy, space, and time and relate them one to another in a great unified field, was neither a physicist nor an astronomer, but a mathematician.

With the aid of a simple diagram we can see more clearly how the many fields of science are in fact related to one another. Since the circle was once considered the perfect geometrical unit we might represent the entire world of science with all its divisions as a great circle.

In the center is a smaller circle or core, representing the field of mathematics. Some scientists insist that mathematics is the very cornerstone of all science; perhaps it would be more accurate to call mathematics the *language* of science, the means we have of describing and relating the phenomena observed in all the branches of science.

Outside this central core I have divided the circle into three sections to represent the three great fields of science: the physical sciences, the life sciences, and the earth sciences. In each of these sections I have filled in some of the major subdivisions or branches, attempting to place them close together or far apart according to their relationship to one another.

You will notice that the dividing lines between these major sections are not solid, but dotted. It would be foolish for instance, to try to erect a solid barrier between organic chemistry as a physical science and genetics or pharmacology as life sciences. Some fields, such as biochemistry or physical chemistry, lie squarely on the dividing lines, and in some places certain scientific disciplines, such as the field of medicine, en-

compass a multitude of branches. This is indicated by shading
on the diagram.

You will also notice certain fields that do not really fit into
any of the three great divisions. These "bridge" sciences, such
as psychology and sociology, are placed in the diagram in
the areas where they seem to fit in best.

I will make no apologies for the shortcomings of this Circle
of Science diagram. It is both incomplete and inaccurate but
it makes its point—that each one of the many divisions of
science is merely a spoke in a great wheel. The world of science
would be incomplete if any one of them were missing. Each is
inseparably linked and related to each of the others, with the
common language and binding force of mathematics at the
center.

The Scientist in the Circle

Thus we can see that science is concerned with the overall
nature of the universe and the natural laws by which it functions. But where does the scientist fit into the Circle of Science?

Working in one field of science or another, the scientist has
one major project: gathering information about the universe
and the way it works, organizing that information so that it
makes sense, and outlining the laws of nature which account
for the things that happen.

Of course, science is more than an assembling of assorted
knowledge, and the scientist has more to do than merely
studying the information which has already been accumulated. This he must unquestionably do; every scientist is first
a student of what has already been learned and proven, or
suspected and partly proven.

But studying what has gone before is not enough. The
scientist is also an investigator, a kind of experimental detective. Using the knowledge already gained as a starting
point, he seeks to expand that knowledge, to follow up clues

uncovered by earlier work, and to add bit by bit to our understanding of how the universe works. Far from sitting in a musty library scratching up old and forgotten knowledge, the scientist works on a vast expanding frontier of understanding and discovery. More than anything else, it is the discovery and research of the scientist that has molded the world that we live in today. It is his work which is responsible for the ever-increasing change that is coming about in our modern way of life.

But not all scientists are doing precisely the same work in the same way, and not all workers in science are working toward precisely the same goals. Certain scientists are concerned solely with increasing our understanding of the laws of nature, and nothing more. They are interested in scientific knowledge for its own sake, not for any practical usefulness it may have for us. Such men, searching out the basic patterns of nature's behavior, are spoken of as "pure" or "theoretical" scientists; their quest for new knowledge without concern for how it may be used is often called "pure" or "basic" research.

Other scientists take the opposite approach in their work. They are concerned with the useful application of scientific knowledge. Given the basic knowledge, they ask, what can be done with it? How can we make it work for us, what will it allow us to do that we could not do before? Or given a problem to solve, how can we use our understanding of science to solve it? The scientists concerned with these questions are spoken of as "applied" scientists, and their search for ways to use scientific knowledge is called "applied" research.

Both pure scientists and applied scientists have important jobs to do; the work of the one is every bit as necessary as the work of the other. As the names imply, the pure scientist traditionally has more rank in the scientific hierarchy, but the dividing lines between pure science and applied science are seldom clear-cut. Often the applied scientist, in looking for a specific answer to a specific problem, may spend months or years doing pure or basic research just to obtain the information he needs to find a solution. And the pure scientist, in uncovering new basic knowledge of the laws of nature, is opening the door for anyone who can find a way to apply it.

But to put scientific knowledge to work for us in any practical way, another kind of worker is needed: the *engineer*. His job is to take into the workshop a working idea that has been tested and proven in the laboratory and design it into an efficient and useful form. Often applied scientists and engineers are working side by side, one developing the principles

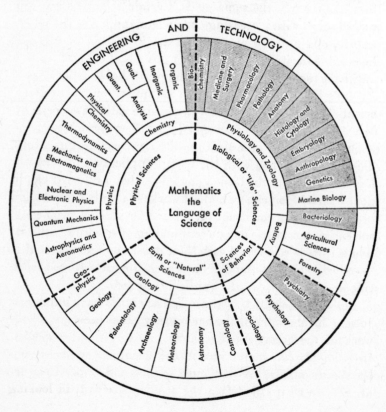

of a new device, the other designing working models. Both are aided by the *technologist* who has certain specialized working skills but lacks the scientific training and background of the scientist or engineer. There is often no fine dividing line between these groups of workers, even though we arbitrarily set one up in our Circle of Science diagram. Much of the training of the engineer is the same as the training of the scientist. He simply has a different job to do from that of the scientist, with different goals to achieve, and different methods altogether of achieving these goals.

For the sake of simplicity we will not try to discuss engineering or the work that engineers do in this book, even though we recognize that their work is as critical to the scientific change in our world as the work of the basic research scientist.

One example will help make clear the relationship among scientists, engineers, and technologists. Basic research in math and physics gave us an understanding of radioactive materials and the forms of energy which they emit, and of the basic relationship between mass and energy. Without that work, we would never have known of the enormous energy stored in the cores of atoms. But once pure science had uncovered these natural laws, applied scientists began seeking out ways to use this knowledge of atomic energy. The development of the first atomic bomb was perhaps the greatest project in applied science that any nation has ever undertaken, and the result was a crude weapon for war. The engineers then refined the form and structure of the bomb, found ways of building it quickly and storing it safely, devised airplanes to carry it, and with the help of the thousands of technologists who worked with them, really made it work. Any break in the chain from pure scientist to applied scientist to engineer and technologist, and World War II might have lasted years longer than it did.

The Expanding Circle

These are the people who are working in the Circle of
Science. It is the work they are doing which is molding the
world we live in. Everywhere we turn we see the change that
science has brought about, and the rate of this change has been
accelerating continuously since the earliest days of science.

In many ways it seems that we are now living in an age
when everything is happening at once. Four hundred years
ago the basic knowledge was being gathered bit by bit,
slowly and laboriously. But as more was learned, people discovered that science could mean newer, better, and easier
ways of doing things. More people became interested in scientific work, both in basic research and in the application of
basic knowledge. Today the changes are coming so fast that
hardly a day goes by without the announcement of some new
discovery that can change our lives.

And this is another fundamental reason that the scientist
seems to be such an unpopular fellow sometimes. Quite naturally, most people do not care much for change. They like
things they can understand, and they like things to stand
still for them. We have all heard of the farmer who had no
qualms as a young man about burning his one-horse shay and
sending old Nellie to the glue factory when Mr. Ford brought
out his horseless carriage, yet twenty years later objected
violently to the "new-fangled" idea of a gear shift in his car!
Once things are settled down, changes are painful to make.

Yet the scientist, more than anyone else, is the man who is
forcing us to make changes. His discoveries are changing
things so rapidly that our feet hardly touch ground any more!
Before, we had a few years to get used to each new idea; now
they keep popping up week by week and day by day.

And naturally the scientist is the one who gets the blame.

It is this enormous growth in our knowledge and use of
science that makes it so important to us to produce new cre-

ative scientists in larger and larger numbers. It has also brought with it some puzzling and perplexing problems to the scientists. With work in science divided into so many specialized fields and categories, one branch of science tends to lose sight of what the other branches are doing. More and more frequently, work being done in one branch of science is being duplicated in other branches simply because nobody knew that it had already been done. Scientists in one field have all they can do to keep abreast of advancements in their own field, without keeping up with all the others too. And all too often the answers desperately needed in one field have already been found in another, and nobody realizes it.

In fact there is a growing need for someone who can keep an eye on the entire spectrum of science as a unit, rather than watching individual trees in the forest. There is a need for the individual who specializes in no one field, but whose knowledge of a number of fields is broad enough to correlate the work being done in one with that being done in another. A. E. Van Vogt, a popular science fiction writer of the last decade, coined the term "Nexialist" to describe such an individual. Within the next few decades we may see the field of correlation of scientific knowledge, the field of Nexialism, growing more and more important, and the Nexialist whose sole job is to know enough about all fields of science to tell where specialized knowledge in one can be used to help in another may well become a key man in our scientific progress.

It is not difficult to see that in this vast, exciting world of scientific discovery there is a growing need for many different kinds of workers with many different degrees of scientific training. You are interested in science and the careers of scientists or you would not be reading this book. Possibly you have been wondering if there really is any place for your particular talent and qualifications in the world of science.

Obviously, the answer is yes. The world of science covers an enormous range of interest. No one with intelligence and imagination could fail to find some interesting corner in that world. This is not to say that anyone with a vague interest in science can expect to become an expert, top-level, exhaustively trained, and brilliant creative scientist. Of all who start on the road to a career in science, only a minority will have the necessary natural equipment—the spark of creativity and the drive to learn how to use it—to become really top-level scientists.

But if you have the slightest inclination toward scientific discipline and thinking, you can be sure of finding a place for yourself at some level in the world of science. It is not even important that you know, to start with, exactly where in the great circle you may ultimately want to focus your interest. Any prospective scientist first must have a broad background of information about all the fields of science. With such a background he can then find his place in whatever field he desires, at whatever level he can achieve, limited only by his intelligence, his creative ability, and the amount and quality of his scientific training.

And in any field in the world of science, at any level, from the most unimaginative technologist to the genius-level "pure thinker," the goal is ultimately the same: the discovery of the ways that nature behaves in an exciting world of wonder and change.

THREE

Training in Science: The First Steps

WITH A BETTER idea of the scope of science in our minds, we can approach the question of preparing for a career in science with a little more confidence and with a clearer concept of the scientist and what he does than the popular stereotype suggests.

As we have seen, science presents us with almost unlimited challenges in a multitude of different and exciting fields. Today we are enjoying the fruit of the scientific discoveries that have been made throughout the past two thousand years, yet the surface has barely been scratched. Like sculptors chipping away at an enormous rock, scientists have been chipping away for centuries at the vast unanswered questions of nature. It is only in the last fifty years that some of the great fundamental answers to these questions have begun to take shape. But finding answers does not seem to reduce the frontier of scientific investigation in the least. Instead, every new scientific discovery opens a hundred new doors and raises a thousand new questions which remain to be answered.

It is the job of the scientist to find the answers. He is both a student of what has been learned before, and a detective or investigator searching for new knowledge and new information. The need for his work is increasing by leaps and bounds.

But how does the scientist go about this search for new knowledge? How does he choose where to begin? How does he tell what he should attempt to do in science and how he should go about trying to do it? What kind of training does he need for this specialized kind of work?

How does a scientist get to be a scientist in the first place? Obviously something must happen to transform an interested and intelligent student with a smattering of knowledge of chemistry, math or biology into a highly trained, creative scientist attempting to reproduce the complex chain reactions of enzyme systems that take place within a living cell, or trying to devise ways to increase the breeder reaction in a radioactive power pile. Any scientist, no matter what his field, has obviously accumulated a great deal of knowledge of a very specialized nature. But the scientist of any stature at all has also accumulated something else: a habit of thinking which has made the discovery of new scientific knowledge possible and which transforms the scientist's work from a mere livelihood into a full and rewarding way of life.

How does this transformation come about?

As a prospective scientist, you may already know the direction that you want to go in science. Possibly you already have in mind one of the great problems or unanswered questions of science which you would like to undertake to answer. If this is true, you are decidedly in the minority. Far more likely you are viewing your period of training in science with many questions and considerable confusion. You know that you must undertake a certain number of years of study for a college degree, and perhaps even years more of study. You realize that your training in science, whatever it may involve, will be costly and demanding, yet you do not even know where in the great circle of science you may finally end up. It is a fact that the great majority of prospective scientists do not "find themselves" in science until they are deeply involved in their scientific education; some unfortunately, never do find themselves.

But for anyone starting training in science, a broad outline picture of the goals of that training would be useful.

In this and succeeding chapters we will attempt to outline the general steps that any scientist in any field must take to obtain his training as a scientist, and the general directions he can go with his training. Later we will consider some of the specialized problems that arise in certain of the different scientific fields and discuss some of the scientific (and nonscientific) tools that will help any prospective scientist achieve his goal.

Up to a certain point, the education and training of any scientist is essentially the same as that for any other. The general goals of scientific training are the same in any field; by the time the scientist is ready for specialization he has already passed the critical point in his training which will determine the kind of scientist he will be.

The Method of Science

Strange as it may seem, the odds are very good that most of you reading this book began your basic training in science a long time ago.

For one thing, you have already begun your acquaintance with the basic language of science—a fundamental groundwork in mathematics. In grade school you learned arithmetic. In high school you were taught the basic elements of algebra, plane geometry, and perhaps calculus. It may never have occurred to you that these courses in math had any relationship to science or scientific training, yet in virtually any field of science some form or another of math is of basic importance.

This does not imply that in order to become a scientist in any field you must be an expert and clever mathematician. In some fields of science, such as physics or physical chemistry, the problem of describing what is going on becomes so complex that scientists working in those areas have no choice but to be competent mathematicians. They can't do their work without real skill in using mathematical tools and techniques. But in other fields, particularly in the life sciences or medicine, the role of mathematics seems almost trivial. Some of the most brilliant work in those fields is being done by scientists who have only the most rudimentary understanding of math, often little more than simple arithmetic.

But for any prospective scientist at any level of scientific training, a clear understanding of the basic mathematical language of science will smooth the way.

In the course of your high school education you have also come into contact with certain other basic science courses. Most high schools require courses in biology and hygiene. Many students also have taken basic courses in chemistry and in physics in high school. Outside the curriculum, many high schools have science clubs and offer opportunities for various forms of field trips and sometimes even basic laboratory work. Many students have developed scientific hobbies of one kind or another. In all such activities, you have obviously had some contact with scientific knowledge and thinking.

But in a less obvious way you have already acquired a kind of groundwork for your future training in science that is far more important than formal courses in math and science. From the day you were born you have been growing up in a society that has long since accepted a certain way of thinking about things, a way of deciding what things are true and what things aren't. This formal method of thinking about things which has become so much a part of our way of life is known throughout the world as "the scientific method."

And the first great goal in the training of a prospective scientist is to make this scientific method of thinking so much a part of his everyday thought procedure that it becomes the only logical and reasonable way to approach the solution of a problem.

Many people are frightened away by this fancy name for a method of solving problems. They think of the scientific method as something strange and mysterious and hard to understand, instead of the simple, logical method of finding reliable answers to questions that it really is.

What is this "scientific method" of thinking, exactly, and why is it important enough to be a major goal of scientific education?

A simple example of the scientific method in use will help answer a number of questions about it. Suppose you have been out trout fishing, using worms for bait, and after several hours you have not even had a nibble. You are certain that there are fish in this particular stream you are fishing; you saw another fisherman bring home a day's limit of trout the day before from the same place you have been fishing, and you are wondering why he caught so many and you have caught none at all.

Puzzled, you yank your line out of the water and just watch the stream for a while. Presently you see fish breaking the surface of the water. Why? What makes them jump up to the surface this way? Several possible explanations for this strange behavior on the part of the fish pass through your mind. Perhaps they are coming up for air. Maybe they are just feeling playful; or possibly there is something about the light that attracts them.

Another idea seems more likely. Perhaps they are snapping at something on the surface of the water. Maybe these trout happen to like insects to eat, and leap up to strike when they see one fly near the surface of the water.

This seems like a good lead, so you think of ways to test it out. You just slapped a mosquito that lit on your arm; now you toss it onto the surface of the water. You see a swirl, and the mosquito is gone. You try it again and the same thing happens. In fact, you find that every time you toss a mosquito onto the surface of the water a fish seems to strike at it. After a few tests in this fashion you come to a conclusion. These trout obviously do not like worms, but they seem to find mosquitoes irresistible.

And the next day when you come back to the stream you bring along some imitation mosquito flies and that night you come home with a limit of trout.

It may seem that the problems of trout fishing are far removed from such things as scientific study, yet we have seen here a simple but valid example of the way the scientific method works. Your problem with the trout began with an apparently mystifying question for which you had no answer. You had been offering the trout the largest, most succulent worms you could find, and yet they stubbornly refused to be tempted. What was the reason for this? You had caught other kinds of fish with worms—why not trout? As in any scientific problem, a question or puzzle came first. You had encountered some form of natural phenomenon which did not seem to make sense, something which you could not understand.

So you set about to explain this puzzle. First you just observed what you could, gathering data about what the trout were up to. This period of observation was critical; without it, you would never have found a solution. But the data you gathered suggested several possible answers. Out of three or four possible explanations for the curious behavior of the

fish you observed, you selected one which seemed the most
reasonable: that the fish might be leaping out of the water
to snap at insects.

Of course, at that point you had no proof that this explanation was any more valid than any of the others; as far
as proof was concerned, the fish might be trying to leap to
the sun for all you knew. In order to be sure you had the
true explanation you needed a method of testing.

It did not take too much thinking to devise a simple experiment to test your hypothesis. You had a mosquito ready
at hand. If you tossed it on the water and it floated down-
stream undisturbed, that would indicate that your hypothesis
was wrong. If the fish struck at the mosquito, that would
suggest that the hypothesis was right. Of course, one trial
would not prove anything; the fish might just happen to
break the surface by chance at the right time. But if you
were to toss mosquito after mosquito onto the water, and see
a fish strike each time, the evidence would be convincing
indeed.

So you conducted the experiment. After a dozen or so
mosquitoes disappeared down a trout's gullet, you began to
feel confident that your explanation was right. All evidence
seemed to indicate that the trout were feeding on mosquitoes.
Finally you put the notion to the acid test by offering the
trout mosquitoes with hooks in their tails, and the reward
for your scientific effort was a good trout dinner.

Here then is the vital core of the work that the scientist
does. He starts with a question, a problem, a puzzle, or phenomenon of nature which he cannot understand. First he
gathers all of the information or *data* about this phenomenon
that he can gather by *observation*. On the basis of what he
observes, he may find several possible explanations or *hypotheses* for the phenomenon in question. Choosing the most

likely of these as a *working hypothesis*, the scientist then
devises *experiments* to test whether the hypothesis really
explains the phenomenon or not. If his experiments seem to
bear out the hypothesis in all respects, it may be considered
"true until proven otherwise." In this state of conditional
acceptance, the explanation is called a *theory*. If the theory
stands up without fail under multiple tests designed to disprove it, holding true time and again, no matter who tests
it, it may eventually be considered a proven law of nature.

You will notice that the scientist does not begin with a
conclusion and then attempt to bend the facts to fit it. He
does not close his mind to the possibility that his theory may
still be wrong even though all of his experiments seem to
substantiate it. If there is a single bit of evidence that does
not fit in with the rest, or a single experiment to test a conclusion which doesn't work out even though a dozen other
tests do, the scientist knows that something is wrong. Somewhere there is a flaw in the conclusions he has drawn, something that he is missing or misinterpreting, and he must go
on from there to revise the theory until it fully and reliably
explains every part of the phenomenon in question.

Obviously, there is nothing magical about such a method
of finding an answer to a problem. Far from being mysterious,
this scientific method is so simple and logical that almost
everyone, scientist or not, uses it in some degree or another
in solving everyday problems. It is a time-tested method of
telling truth from nonsense, and proving it. As such, it is
the method that has been used to establish virtually everything that we know about our universe and the way in which
it works.

We are so used to the concept of proving things by means
of experiment and evidence today that it is hard to believe
what a staggering idea this was when it first appeared. Un-

til men began using this scientific method of demonstrating the truth of their hypotheses, there was no way in the world to distinguish truth from nonsense. Before the scientific method was devised, men drew conclusions on the basis of sheer guesswork and deep meditation, and then wrenched and twisted the observed facts until they fitted the conclusions. Like the legendary Procrustes, who stretched or cut off his victims' legs to make them fit into his bed, the early scientists and philosophers tried to squeeze the behavior of nature into the molds that suited them; they managed quite well as long as they carefully ignored the things that didn't fit. Plato used this Procrustean bed technique when he assumed for the sake of neatness that the circle was the most perfect course of movement, thus setting the stage for two thousand years of confusion about the movement of the planets in the heavens. The idea of experimental testing to prove or disprove a conclusion occurred to the early Greeks, but such experimentation was somehow considered beneath their dignity. Even such a simple idea as the relationship between cause and effect was alien to early men. They simply didn't recognize that an unbroken chain of cause and effect ran throughout nature and governed its happenings.

It was not until the scientific method of experimentation to test conclusions was firmly established that science began to grow and that our understanding of the laws of nature began to expand. This method is still the basis of all scientific investigation. The first great goal of your training in science will be to teach you how to use this method of thinking.

Imagination in Science

But the training of a would-be scientist has still another goal. In order to use the scientific method effectively, you must obviously know how to think. This in itself is hard enough work, but something more than just thinking is required. Training in science must also teach you to *think with imagination.*

Some of the greatest discoveries in all the history of science have been made for no apparent logical reason whatever. Men have worked for years trying to solve perplexing problems, and then suddenly found the answers standing before them. Time after time great discoveries have resulted from "accidental" observations, and time after time scientists have made almost magical leaps to just precisely the right conclusions when there were multitudes of other conclusions that might have seemed more likely.

In many ways this strange ability to pull "accidental" discoveries out of a hat is one of the most puzzling and confusing qualities of the scientist. It doesn't happen just occasionally; it happens constantly, and to the non-scientist it seems a little like outright magic. After all, how could anyone be trained to guess correctly most of the time? How could any amount of scientific training explain the "accidental discovery" that yields up the solution to a perplexing problem?

The answer lies in the kind of thinking that these men are capable of. Invariably scientists are curious men; if they weren't they wouldn't be scientists. Invariably they are also imaginative men. The great "accidental discoveries" are no accidents, and the "educated guesses" are ninety-five per cent education and only five per cent guess. The whole process of education in science seeks to prepare the prospective scientist, not just to think but to use imagination and curiosity in his thinking. Seeds which fall on a barren hillside grow poorly if they grow at all; seeds planted in fertile tilled ground can grow handsomely. Training in science is intended to prepare the sort of mind in which ideas can grow and imagination function.

Discipline in Science

But there is still another goal of scientific education. Just as specific courses of study cannot teach imagination or force students to think imaginatively, there are no courses that can teach the sort of discipline which is necessary to transform an alert, intelligent student into a creative and useful scientist. Yet if any one thing is more critical than anything else to the education of the scientist, it is discipline in his thinking.

By discipline here I am not speaking in terms of spankings or withheld allowances as punishments for doing things wrong. There is an enormous difference between productive thinking to find the solution to a problem and vacant nonproductive woolgathering. The difference is discipline—the control of one's thinking capacity to make it do what one wants it to do.

A scientist cannot afford to be sloppy in his thinking. He cannot afford at any time to confuse assumptions with facts, or guesswork with truth. The use of the scientific method to find a valid answer to a problem is absolutely pointless unless the reasoning is rigidly disciplined and controlled every step of the way. Above all, the scientist must be able to be almost fanatically honest and objective about his work. He dare not deceive himself by fitting facts to conclusions. He must be willing to submit everything he does to the scrutiny of his colleagues, and any lapse from rigid control of his thinking will render his work valueless. This discipline that science demands is nothing more nor less than self-discipline. If you lack the capacity for self-discipline, no amount of scientific training will ever instill it. But given the capacity in the first place, your training in science will constantly encourage you to improve your control and will force you to think logically and productively. You will learn to reject unsupported opinions, guesses and groundless assumptions, and to settle only for facts which can be demonstrated to be true.

This sort of discipline is essential to any kind of scientific work. But it is not something that can be turned off at night when you come home from the laboratory and turned on again at nine o'clock the next morning. It must become a way of thinking and a way of life. The scientist by his very nature drives a hard bargain. He will not settle for substitutes, half truths, frauds, or falsehoods. He beats his way through a jungle of them in his work; it is only natural that he will fight them just as much in his everyday life.

The Pattern of Training

This in a nutshell is what your education in science will seek to accomplish: first, to train you in the basic principles of scientific method of investigation; second, to develop your imagination and curiosity and to teach you how to use them in your thinking; and finally, to instill in your mind the rigid discipline and control of thinking which will make your work in science creative and useful.

It does not matter whether you will ultimately be working as an astronomer or a biologist, a doctor, a physicist, or an archaeologist. The basic goals of your scientific training will be the same. For some of you the training has already started. For others, these concepts may be completely foreign, and you will have a longer way to go.

Certainly, this is a great deal for any education program to try to accomplish. How can it be done? How far into this scientific training will you want to go? How can you tell where to start, and once started, when is the time to stop? What sort of a formal program will your training in science involve?

In general, your training in science will follow a series of increasingly difficult steps, each one leading closer to the overall goal. As you take each step, you will be able to evaluate how well you are doing and will have the opportunity to judge whether or not you should go on to the next step. In some cases the decision at each step will be entirely your own to make; you will either find your introduction to science so exciting—and be doing so well in the work—that you wouldn't think of stopping, or you will realize clearly that you have gone as far as you care to go. Often, however, part of the decision is made for you. Throughout your training as a scientist your work will constantly be observed and evaluated by your professors and teachers. If your work is good, you will find endless encouragement to carry on with it, but if there seems to be no promise for you in the next step along the line, the odds are good that you will not be permitted to take it. This may seem at first a very arbitrary and undemocratic process, and indeed it is. But in the training of scientists no one has an automatic right to advancement, only the right that he has earned on his own merit. The whole of scientific training is a process of natural selection in a way, the winnowing of the chaff from the grain, encouraging those with more ability to carry on and those with less to find places at lower levels of training.

The first step which anyone entering into a scientific career must accomplish is the basic background work to be obtained in four years of undergraduate college training.

Most colleges or universities make a sharp distinction in their curricula between the programs in the arts and the sciences. In some ways this is unfortunate; the scientist badly needs a background in the arts—history, literature, languages, and music—just as a student of the arts needs a background in the basic physical sciences. As we will see later, there are some compelling reasons for the would-be scientist to ignore these distinctions during the college years and, if necessary, deliberately seek out certain parts of the liberal arts program. But for the most part your attention will be focused on obtaining a broad background of general information in the sciences during these years.

First, you will have a certain amount of training in mathematics, even though skill in math may not be a critical factor in the field of science you ultimately choose. You will be introduced to the important mathematical tools that are available for every scientist to use—algebra, analytical geometry, and calculus. You will learn techniques for using this universal language of science, but more important, in mathematics you will make your acquaintance with the kind of rigid logical thinking which you will need throughout your scientific career.

You will also become acquainted with certain of the major fields of science, particularly with chemistry, physics, and biology. These are the basic laboratory sciences, the groundwork of a hundred specialty fields. In each of these sciences you will be learning a great deal that has already been discovered and established. You will study what is already known of the relationship of mass and energy, of the basic building blocks of matter and how they interact, and of the structure and function of living creatures.

You will also learn how to use certain kinds of laboratory tools, and how to perform a number of extremely useful laboratory procedures. You will have your first formal training in the scientific method of observation, experiment, and conclusion-drawing. You will learn something of the history of scientific discovery and will repeat in the laboratory many of the classical experiments which have led to great scientific discoveries in the past.

For the prospective scientist, these four years of college are devoted almost entirely to building a background in science. Your work here will require very little original or creative thinking. Your time will be spent learning what is already known, obtaining a general understanding of scientific method, and encountering a taste of scientific discipline. Many of you will end your formal scientific training with your undergraduate degree. If you do, you will find work in almost any scientific field where this background training can be put to use.

But this undergraduate college "basic training" does not prepare you for the really important critical function of the scientist: the use of this background, these tools, and this training in scientific method to do original scientific work.

This is a critical decision you will face at the end of your undergraduate work, whether to end your formal training in science here and use your background education as it stands, or to go ahead into graduate work in one field of science or another. If you have the ability, intelligence, ambition, and curiosity to do original and creative work in science, you would be wasting your talents to stop at this point; if not, further training will only be a waste of your time and money. But how can you possibly tell this? How can you judge your own abilities so objectively?

Of course sometimes you can't—but you will have certain clues to guide you. You will by then have considerable contact with the sciences themselves and the atmosphere of the laboratory. How much did you really like that contact? Was it merely tolerable, or was it exciting and stimulating? How well did you do in terms of grades? How much did you find unanswered, how many disturbing and intriguing holes did you find in your acquaintance with science? If your curiosity was well satisfied by the contact, you would be wise to think twice about going further; but if it was merely whetted, nothing could persuade you to stop.

Often your first year of graduate work will help you be certain of your decision. In the course of your four-year "survey" of the world of science, you will have found certain fields that appeal to you more than others. Now, having finished undergraduate work, you take the next step, beginning work for a master's degree, concentrating your attention and your energy on some special field of science.

Even yet, you will not be doing original work of your own, in most cases, but will be working on problems that other scientists have already begun investigation on. Still, you will have more freedom and encouragement to do original thinking about such problems, and begin to make some real contribution to the progress of the program you are working in. With your interest centered on a problem in a single specialized field of science, you will have the opportunity to explore that field far more thoroughly than the undergraduate "survey" courses allowed. In science more than anywhere else, you learn far more by *doing* than by *hearing* or *reading* or *being taught*. You learn from the scientist who started the program how the problem arose and why he became interested in it. You begin digging into the specialized background needed to understand the problem and enter into the research program actively, learning specialized skills and tools as you need them. If certain forms of math are necessary, you learn the math. If a more basic understanding of metabolic chain reactions would help, you find more information in these lines. You may even notice unexplored avenues of approach toward the solution of the problem, and start tentatively formulating your own experiments to explore some of them.

In fact, your first postgraduate year of study toward a master's degree will be very much of a proving ground, pointing up your own abilities and weaknesses, and crystallizing your interests more sharply. Even though your final report or *thesis* may be a detailed discussion of the progress of someone else's research program, it will reflect your own aptitude for higher-level scientific work and your own readiness to undertake original work of your own.

The next step in your scientific training—working for a doctorate or a Ph.D. degree in your chosen field of science—is the most difficult and demanding of all. At this point you leave other people's work behind and select your own problems to investigate. By this time you have a thorough background in your field and a great deal of skill in using the special tools of scientific investigation. By this time also the scientific method of approach to problems of nature has become so much a part of your thinking that it seems the only natural way to start searching for answers. Whatever your field, be it astronomy or chemistry, physiology or geology, you select a problem which has never been solved, a puzzle which has never been pieced together, and you set about to find a solution on your own. You set up your own approach to studying the problem. You make your own observations, devise your own experiments, keep your own records, draw your own conclusions, and, finally, prepare your conclusions for publication in an exhaustive report. That report, known as a *doctoral thesis*, will document your own original contribution to the mass of scientific knowledge, the fragment of new knowledge that you have uncovered in the field where you are working.

In many fields in the arts, doctoral theses are notoriously

long, dull discussions of obscure topics, of interest to no one
but the student and his professor, and promptly buried deep
in the archives and forgotten as soon as they are written and
accepted. The work done for a scientific doctoral degree is
not likely to be so obscure or so quickly buried. More often
than not, this is the first step along the road of scientific investigation that the fledgling scientist will be following for
the rest of his life. He may take side roads or detours; he
may find his first approaches amateurish, poorly thought
out, or frankly hopeless, but often his doctoral work is a
very real and useful contribution to the world's stockpile of
scientific knowledge.

Needless to say, of the thousands of young people who
enter scientific training at the undergraduate college level,
relatively few will make their way up the ladder to achieve
their doctoral degrees. Most find their proper places at a
lower level of training. College training in science and even
the work for a master's degree is within the scope of almost
anyone with average or slightly above average intelligence
and ability. Relatively few prospective scientists have the
special creative ability and the exceptional drive, intelligence,
and determination to carry through to doctoral degrees. Some
of these qualities can be deliberately cultivated and developed,
but sheer native ability cannot. I could no more make myself
a Doctor of Philosophy in Mathematics just by wanting
to become one than I could make myself a pitcher for the
Yankees.

In many ways the achievement of a Ph.D. in a scientific
discipline is far more difficult than the achievement of an
M.D. degree. The Ph.D. candidate must undergo trial by
fire; he must prove his ability to perform original creative
work, while the M.D. need have no creative ability, merely

a highly skilled ability to put other people's discoveries into operation.

Yet anyone who is interested in a career in scientific work should at least look toward the top of the ladder. Somewhere between the bottom and the top he will find the place where his ability and his intelligence meet the demands perfectly. Whatever the appropriate stopping place, he will find work he can do well and a challenge he can pursue.

This then, in broad outline, is the formal program any scientist will follow in obtaining his training in science, from the basic training in college, through the more specialized training needed for a master's degree, to the highly specialized creative work required for a doctorate. But what does each step in this training program mean in terms of a career and future? How can you guess what goal to set for yourself as you start at the bottom of the ladder? Will you best be fitted to become a technologist or to carry on to the top of the ladder for a Ph.D? What kind of work could you expect to find at each level of scientific training?

Possibly you will not have the answers to all of these questions when you begin—but it would be wise to have at least a tentative goal in mind and an idea of what each level of achievement in scientific training can offer you. In the following chapter, we will consider in more detail the various levels of scientific training and discuss some of the advantages and disadvantages that each level has to offer, before going on to details of training in the different broad fields of science.

FOUR

Training in Science: Qualifications and Goals

ANYONE WHO HAS decided on a career in science must follow the formal program of scientific training we have just discussed. The way may differ a little from one broad field of science to another, but the general direction is the same for any field. Yet perhaps the most confusing and perplexing problem that any prospective scientist must face is where to set his goal—just where to begin in his education for science and where to plan to stop.

In other kinds of careers there is no such problem. The would-be lawyer may not know exactly what kind of law he will want to practice when he starts his training, but he knows that he must go to law school and pass bar examinations before he can practice *any* kind of law. The would-be doctor may not decide on surgery, or general practice, or psychiatry until his medical training is almost complete, but no matter what position he wants in medicine he must first complete his premedical training, go to medical school, and serve as a hospital intern.

But scientific work in general has no such all or nothing requirements as bar examinations or a medical license. The prospective scientist can find some kind of place in a scientific pursuit after one year of college as well as after four; there are no clear-cut upper and lower limits to his scientific training. You know that some degree of education and training in science is necessary, of course—but how much? If there are scientists working at all levels of training, where should you set your sights? What do the different levels of scientific training mean in terms of kind of work, responsibility, prestige, salary, and security? If we look for a moment at the various levels of scientific training, we see each level has different requirements. Each offers certain advantages as well as certain drawbacks.

On one hand, an individual with no more than a high school education can find work in science and may have the chance to make his own small contribution to the advancement of scientific knowledge, if only by relieving a more highly-trained scientist of some of the routine parts of his work which do not require specialized training or imagination. At the other extreme, a scientist with a Ph.D. is expected to be making significant contributions, to be actively engaged in creative scientific work, and to be teaching, leading, and inspiring the scientists with lesser degrees of training.

Yet there are thousands of scientists with only bachelor's or master's degrees who are actively engaged in truly creative scientific work.

The Pyramid of Achievement

One way of thinking of the various levels of scientific work which one might achieve is to consider them as levels in a pyramid, with the basically untrained technicians at the bottom level and the highly specialized genius-thinkers at the top.

Each level up this pyramid of careers in science requires more training, more native ability, more skill, and more imagination than the level below. Each level also has fewer people in it than the step below. Each level contains a certain number of scientific people who would very much like to move up to a higher level, but can't quite make it because of some impediment or another—the lack of ability, the cost of further training, the time that such training would require, or what-have-you. But each level also contains many others who are happy in the level of work they are doing and have no desire to go higher.

The bottom level of the pyramid is made up of the thousands of basically untrained people who are working in some way or another as technicians in scientific laboratories, engineering shops, and drafting rooms wherever scientific work is being done. Even though they may be highly skilled in their individual jobs, these people can rarely be considered scientists. For the most part, their education has ended with a high school diploma, or with one or two years of college; they bring no specialized knowledge, ability, or training to their work.

The workers on this level have very few of the advantages connected with careers in science. In a given job, they have no choice in what they do. They work for wages, doing the jobs they are hired to do. They have no particular security in those jobs; the work they are doing could be done by almost anyone, and if one worker does not measure up to what is required of him, he is soon replaced by someone who does. These people work a nine-to-five day, five days a week. Many of them gain very little from their work except a moderate living.

But if these people at the bottom level of the pyramid do not get much out, it must be said that they don't have to put much in, either. The kind of work they are doing requires no special education, training, ability, or intelligence. It burdens them with very little responsibility. Above all, they are not expected to contribute original ideas or creative think-ing. Generally speaking, they couldn't if they wanted to, which is the reason they are at the bottom of the pyramid.

With the completion of four years of college training in one of the broad fields of science, the would-be scientist moves up a level in the pyramid. With a bachelor's degree and the training it represents, he finds his career opportunties in science enormously improved. In all fields of scientific work the bachelor of science finds the welcome mat out; thousands each year step directly from the college graduation halls into jobs in the various fields of science.

These people can often justly be called scientists. Their work may not be highly specialized, but with their background training in science they are equipped to join the scientific team. Some continue on to work at a college or university in an academic capacity, teaching, doing research, and often studying for advanced degrees. Others take jobs in industries that need scientifically trained people. Many such industries are carrying on very specialized scientific work and provide on-the-job training in their specialized fields for those with promise. Others simply put college-trained scientists to work on research projects that are already under way, assuming the graduate's ability to pick up what additional training he needs to do the work.

If you are working in this level of the pyramid, odds are good that you will spend your time working on assigned problems, carrying out research work that has been devised by others and planned out for you to do. You will have little opportunity for creative scientific work at this level. Without the specialized training of graduate work in your field, you will be better equipped to follow the direction of others than to strike off in original research of your own.

Suppose, for example, that one of the pharmaceutical

companies wants to develop a new type of pain-relieving drug. Such a company would have scientists at all levels on its research and development team. The program to develop a drug with certain properties and no unfortunate side effects would be outlined first by the highly trained and experienced scientists on the team. These scientists, often with Ph.D. or M.D. degrees, would decide the general lines the research should follow. Directed by them, the rest of the research staff, with lesser degrees of training, would undertake the research under their guidance.

If you were working for such a company with a bachelor's degree, you would contribute as much to the project as your training and ability would permit. Generally speaking, at this level you might have a good deal of contact with the creative work of science but would not be called upon to provide it yourself. As you worked, you would learn more about the field in which you were working. Your salary would be moderate, with a definite top limit, and your security in your job would also be moderate.

Yet at this level you can expect to participate in some of the intangible rewards of scientific work. As answers are found, you can take satisfaction that you have contributed to finding them. It is these intangible rewards—the satisfaction of achievement, the enjoyment of the work you are doing, the excitement of scientific research and discovery, which are the crowning attractions of a career in science at any level. If you are doing work which is stimulating and exciting, and which you thoroughly enjoy, the tangible rewards—such as the salary, the security and the professional status—are not so important. If you are primarily interested in making an excellent salary or in finding a position that offers you life-long security or personal power, you should be warned that you can find these far more readily somewhere else than in a career in science. It is well to realize from the start that the reward you will obtain from a scientific career is not so much the living that you will make from it as the fun and excitement of the work that provides the living.

If the level of work that you can hope to do in science with just a bachelor's degree sounds limited, remember that I am pointing out *probabilities*, not *possibilities*. The lack of an advanced degree in science may be an impediment to advancement in your scientific career, but it is by no means an insurmountable barrier. At any level of the pyramid from the bottom up, real native ability and original thinking will in the long run command more attention than any affidavit of formal education. The history of science is full of accounts of men and women, truly great scientists, whose achievements have far outstripped their formal education. If you have the ability and the drive to use it, there is virtually no limit to what you can achieve in science, regardless of the college degree you may hold.

A good friend of mine got off to the most inauspicious of starts in his scientific career. As a college student he spent more time writing musical comedies for the college players than he did studying for his degree in mathematics. His practice was to ignore his classwork to the limit, and then spend two nights before each semester exam plowing through the work of the previous half year as fast as he could. Immediately after graduation he found himself a Naval Reserve officer, and by good fortune was assigned to a computer section in Washington. Musical comedies were forgotten as he turned his very considerable mathematical talent to the intricate problems of electronic computer programming, translating problems into the kind of language that the computer could use. Within two years he had become an expert in this phase of computer work, and he was retained by the govern-

ment on a high civil service rating to continue this work. Soon
he was not only an expert programmer but was acting as a
consultant to Ph.D. mathematicians, showing them new ways
to solve programming problems of their own. Five years after
graduation from college he was turning down tempting research offers from the major computer manufacturers in
order to go to England to teach programming to the computer men there who had machines they did not know how
to use. His writing ability has resulted in some scientific
papers on computer programming that are wonders of clarity
in a field noted for its dense prose.

The fact that this man barely squeaked by with a bachelor's degree from a college with an inferior math department
will never stand in the way of his scientific career. He has
the natural ability and the capacity for concentration and
self-discipline which will compensate a thousand times over
for his lack of formal training.

But for such an individual to stop his formal training
with a bachelor's degree is most unusual. Most scientists with
that kind of ability and drive move on up to the next level
of the pyramid, taking advanced training for master's degrees and doctorates. With a master's degree and the specialized training that it implies, a scientist finds the doorways
into creative scientific research opening up for him. Univer
sities welcome him into their teaching programs and provide
laboratories where he can work in original research of his
own. Industries seek him out eagerly to work in their laboratories, offering him salaries designed to tempt him away from
the ivory towers of the universities. He has taken more time
and paid more money for his training than the average bachelor of science, but in return he can command greater professional status, better salary, and more freedom to choose his
work in science than most men with bachelor's degrees.

The ones who go on for doctoral degrees in science are all too rare. In a recent survey of the status of advanced scientific education in the United States, the National Science Foundation found that in comparison to the 7,000 M.D. degrees which were granted in one sample year, only 986 individuals were granted Ph.D.'s in chemistry, 470 in physics, 230 in mathematics, 23 in astronomy and 10 in meteorology. Of course, this reflected to some degree the lack of interest in science that existed in our country at the time. To a much greater degree it reflected the hard work, natural ability, and determination required to achieve a doctorate in any scientific field. The man with a Ph.D. in science has proven his ability in scientific research and thinking. He stands at the top of the pyramid in scientific training. He is a specialist in his field, and almost invariably he has selected a major direction or a major problem in his field on which he wishes to work.

While it is true that there are relatively few positions requiring the specialized training of Ph.D.'s, there are still fewer people available to fill those positions. As a result, the Doctor of Philosophy in any scientific field can command a top salary and a great deal of independence in the work he wants to do. He commands the highest respect of his profession. More often than not he can decide first what line of research he wishes to engage in, confident that he can find someone to pay him a salary while he does it.

But the Ph.D. degree in science is not entirely a carte blanche that allows one to wander off in any direction he chooses. There are certain drawbacks too. The doctorate requires the investment of an additional four or five years in education and training over and above four years of college. This is a period of long hours, intensive study, hard work, and very little income. If the scientist is married and has a family (as is often the case) it means skimping and saving, with everybody pitching in to help. The picture of the scientist as a shabby, worn, down-at-heel appearing individual is unfortunately no joke to many doctoral candidates in the sciences.

And if his material rewards are ultimately greater than those of the lesser-trained scientist, the Ph.D. carries a greater burden of responsibility. Wherever he works, he is expected to produce—to contribute steadily to the growth of new scientific knowledge. In a very real sense, the responsibility for progress in science lies squarely in his hands: he is the spearhead, expected to scout new pathways, inspire his fellow scientists, and lead the way.

His work has many hidden pitfalls. It is too easy for him to become engrossed in (to him) fascinating but essentially meaningless and insignificant minutiae. He may work for years fruitlessly exploring a blind alley, and then find it extremely difficult to back out and start over again. Most treacherous of all the pitfalls is the phenomenon of scientific "authority"; too many brilliant and top-level scientists have been trapped by their own success, starting to work on promising theories, making themselves "authorities" in their fields, and then spending the rest of their lives attacking, debunking, and suppressing the ideas of anyone who does not agree with them, regardless of any real merit those ideas might have.

But relatively few top-ranking men fall into such traps as these, and it is a tribute to the kind of minds that scientific training develops that the men and women at the top of the pyramid are the valid, rightful leaders of science, placed there on the strength of their proven abilities and not by popularity contests, political influence, pleasing personalities, or money. If the process of selection of top-level scientists seems coldhearted and undemocratic, it is well to remember that there is no "entrenched privilege" in science. If you have what it takes, you can drive to the top; if you don't, you will never make it.

These, then, are the levels of training in science, with some of the rewards and drawbacks they imply. But throughout all levels of scientific endeavor, there is an unwritten obligation which all scientists feel, although very little is ever said about it. I am speaking of the *obligation to teach*. Few scientists of any stature in the country fail to spend at least some of their time teaching others the knowledge and skill they have acquired. No amount of money can buy the ingredients of a good scientific education; too much of the training that a scientist obtains is given to him, generously and eagerly, by the men and women who are teaching him. Once it is received, the scientist feels the tacit obligation to pass his training on to any scientist who is deeply involved and fascinated by his work. To a scientist, teaching seems as natural and necessary as breathing, and any scientist is eager to pass on what he has learned, either to students in formal university classes and laboratories, in publications of his work in scientific journals, or simply in personal contact with younger scientists who are working with him.

The Scientist at Work

Whatever your training in science, from the lowest level to the highest, you will most probably find your place in the world of science in one of three great areas: the academic life, government work, or work in industry.

Each of these areas needs scientists badly. Each absorbs people with all degrees of training in science, and each has its own special advantages and drawbacks. In planning a career in science you will want to consider the opportunities each of these outlets has to offer as well as the disadvantages to be found in each. And in considering the work of scientists in the academic life, government, and industry, we run headlong into the conflict between pure and applied science.

Most people think of the scientist in an academic background, working in a college or university and engaged both in laboratory research and teaching. Many of you may be thinking of the academic life as the most desirable way in which to use your scientific training. Here, it might seem, you should be free to follow up whatever lines of research your fancy dictates, free of the problems and competition that exist outside the ivory-tower atmosphere of the university.

To a certain degree this kind of thinking is perfectly valid. Certainly the colleges and universities are more interested in the goals of pure science—the accumulation of scientific knowledge solely for its own sake—than many industries, which must make their scientific research pay off some way in dollars and cents, or the government, which has its own essentially nonscientific axe to grind. In the academic atmosphere the scientist may not feel quite as much pressure to produce work which is valuable in terms of salable new products, or bigger and better bombs. A university scientist may be able to follow out lines of research which have no obvious value whatever, other than expanding the horizon of our understanding of nature.

Yet the scientist in an academic career will find a number of unsuspected special annoyances to cope with in the microcosm of a college or university. Too often he finds himself helplessly embroiled in petty campus politics and bickering. While he may be free to conduct his work in peace, he has such things as "tenure" to think about—until he has reached a certain professional status, he may be vulnerable to being pitched out on his ear every year when his contract comes up for renewal. He must be concerned with advancement up the academic ladder, and he may find himself under great pressure to publish the results of his work whether they are ready for publication or not, solely for the sake of prestige. He may select his projects without interference—but he may also find that his advancement on the faculty depends upon the success or failure of the work that he is doing. For some people, the academic life is perfectly suited to their personalities and to the kind of work in science that they want to do. For others, it can become intolerable, and these must leave and find work in other areas.

Quite a considerable number of scientists work directly or indirectly for the federal government. They may be found in the laboratories of universities or medical schools or industrial plants, but their salaries are paid by federal grants which supply them with the means to carry on their work.

Oftentimes these scientists have more freedom in the selection of the work they want to do than anyone else in science. More and more the people controlling the federal grants and private foundation money are recognizing that basic research and pure science must be supported, even if it produces no immediate tangible results that can be put to use. But the scientist working for the government has his problems too. In order to carry on his work, his funds must be renewed each year, and in order to gain renewal he must be able to justify in some way the amount of money spent during the previous year. A project supported year after year may be dropped cold, with no apparent regard to the importance of the project, simply because Congress cut appropriations that year! And on many government-supported projects, scientists have the additional burden of security clearance to face and national policies of secrecy to struggle with. For some scientists these annoyances are not particularly disturbing, but others grow embittered by the nonscientific thinking that interferes with their work, and it sometimes seems that the government has done everything it could think of to drive scientists *away* from government service. But at least there is some hope that the desperate need for scientists will force a change in the more foolish of government restrictions that hamstring their scientific workers.

Industry was once considered the ugly duckling among outlets for scientific training, but in recent years this tendency of scientists to look down their noses at the scientific opportunities in industrial laboratories has begun to mellow. American industry has been presenting increasingly attractive opportunities to young people with sound scientific training, and more and more scientists are finding fruitful and satisfying work in the laboratories of private industrial corporations.

It might seem at first glance that industry, with its ever present concern for new products that will sell and its ever present worry about the cost of such products, would be diametrically opposed to the idea of scientific research solely for the sake of knowledge. And it is very true that the major interest of industry is in the application of scientific principles and discoveries to salable products, not in knowledge for its own sake. No company could afford to pay salaries to scientists, equip laboratories, and hire large staffs of engineers and technicians to put the scientists' discoveries to work if the scientists found nothing of value in terms of useful products. For many years industry was unpopular among scientists, who liked to think of their work as a sort of a sacred calling and considered the great companies to be mere scavengers and exploiters of their hard work and dedicated labors.

But in recent years many great industries have begun to realize that their greatest hope for the future lies not in rigidly controlled applied-research programs aimed at specific goals that would pay off quickly, but rather in basic scientific research which might not pay its way now, but might pay off a thousand times over in the long pull. In very practical terms of dollars and cents, the quick-profit research programs have proven far less valuable than the basic long-term programs that opened up new fields with hundreds or thousands of possible products. Such "long-term gamble" thinking began in certain of the communications, electronics, and aircraft industries, but nowhere is there a better example than in the booming pharmaceutical industry.

High blood pressure has always been one of the greatest unsolved mysteries of medicine. Thousands of men have spent their lives studying this disease in an attempt to find out what causes it and how it might be controlled. Out of this mass of research work came a number of promising clues, and the pharmaceutical companies put their own scientists to work to develop drugs which would help to control high blood pressure according to these clues.

But each of these clues was only part of the answer, and a small part at that. The riddle still had not been solved. Once certain basic drugs were developed, the pharmaceutical houses that developed them had no place to go, so they began refining those drugs, attempting to make them work better. Some of them did, but soon even that road came to an end, with all of its possibilities exhausted. It became obvious that there would be no more new basic drugs to be used against high blood pressure until science could better understand what caused the disease and thus guess what might control it.

And this meant basic, grinding, unregimented pure research into the fundamental structure and function of living organisms. The lack of understanding of the basic causes of this disease was a solid brick wall that could not be surmounted by the quick-profit method of applied research. The answer might take years or decades or even centuries to be found—if it could be found at all.

It was—and still is—an enormous challenge to the drug manufacturers. But more and more they have begun to realize that they would have been far ahead now if they had invested the money and hired the scientists to study the basic mechanisms of the disease in the first place, rather than developing stopgap drugs for quick profits in hopes that pure research would keep ahead of them. Many of the drug companies are meeting the challenge now; the result could mean the final conquest of a dreadful killer.

And more and more industries now are giving their topnotch scientists a free hand to work in any direction they feel like working, without worrying about coming up with results the company can use immediately. To the industries the idea begins to make sense: give a crew of intelligent, imaginative, and creative scientists room enough to work in, and the results of their work in one way or another will suggest the applications that will keep the industries in business. It was a tough one for hardheaded businessmen to swallow—yet those that tried it have found to their amazement that their gamble is paying off. Discoveries turn up in the most unexpected places, and completely undreamed-of applications are found for basic research that seems to have no application at all. Such a trend is encouraging to scientists, and at the rate scientific progress is changing our world, it seems likely that the trend will gather momentum rapidly. Such a marriage between pure science and competitive industry cannot help but benefit everyone; it may be that within a few years industry will be offering young scientists the richest of all opportunities for pure scientific work.

The Goal Ahead

With so many opportunities available at so many different levels of training in science, the would-be scientist just starting his training should be in an excellent position to set his sights, make plans for his education, and feel confident that he will find the right place for his talents in the world of science. But guessing the proper level to aim for in advance can be a real problem. How can you judge whether to aim for a bachelor's degree or aspire to a doctorate in your chosen field? How can you tell along the way when you have reached your limit, and should stop and put your training to work rather than try to go on further?

These are questions that plague every individual starting off in a scientific career. You badly need a goal to strike for, but the goal that you set should at least be within your capabilities, or you will be risking discouragement and failure. What are the qualities and qualifications that the prospective scientist will need to carry him on through the long and difficult training period he must undergo?

For anyone undertaking a career in science, a certain degree of intelligence is certainly going to be a help. The would-be scientist will have to absorb a great deal of information of increasing complexity as he goes along; he needs the intellectual capacity to learn things easily, to retain a certain amount of what he learns, and to use what he learns to help him learn more.

This does not mean that you must necessarily be brilliant, nor even that you need to have a particularly prodigious memory. An I.Q. high above average may be a help, but it is by no means a necessity for a successful and even brilliant career in science.

Far more important than the intelligence is the ability to control the intelligence you have and make it work for you.

And this single quality can make or break the prospective scientist from the start.

I knew two young men in college who were different from each other in every possible way except for one thing: each of them was interested in a career in science.

Of the two almost anyone would have given Paul the better odds for success. Paul's high school record was most promising; his grades were straight A's, he was a member of the honor society, twice president of his class, and valedictorian at his commencement. He came to college on a full scholarship after taking college entrance examinations. There was no question that Paul was brilliant, and he doubtless was interested in science. He could run circles around me in any kind of argument, a pleasant personable fellow with a real idea-factory for a mind. It seemed that the sky was the limit for him.

But there were two things wrong with Paul: he was lazy, and he was restless. He had long since learned that he didn't have to stir himself very much to get A's in high school. He had discovered that a quick mind, a quick tongue, and a pleasing personality could save him the trouble of a great deal of hard work. He learned surprisingly fast—but he had no idea what to do with what he learned after he learned it, and he tended to forget almost as fast as he learned.

He could not sit down to work at a book for more than twenty minutes at a stretch before he was up and about, going out for a cup of coffee, turning on the radio, strumming on his banjo, or engaging somebody in brilliant argument. When he came up against a problem that did not yield instantly to his quick thinking, he would lose interest in it, and he turned rapidly from one enthusiasm to the next. He was popular on campus halfway through his freshman year, but almost flunked out of school before the year was over.

The second year he got hold of himself enough to stay in school, but he still insisted on using his quick mind to save himself from doing any work. He never did learn to maintain one interest long enough to do anything with it.

Paul started college as a science major. He graduated with a degree in business administration. He is now public relations manager for a big aircraft firm in the East, with a high salary and many admirers. But he is decidedly not a scientist.

Andy was as different from Paul as he could be. A big 210-pounder, Andy had played guard on the high school football team, and brought a record of B's and C's with him to college. Andy was not brilliant; in fact, he gave the impression that he was downright dull. He learned things slowly and painfully and had to dig hard for every morsel that he absorbed.

But Andy was not afraid of hard work, and Andy was stubborn. He was welcomed with open arms by the coach on the freshman football squad, but he decided after the first season to drop football from his schedule because it took up too much time. He dug into his studies with a vengeance, churning away for hours on a problem that Paul would have disposed of in a few moments or tossed aside. To his friends Andy seemed slow and stolid, a sort of earnest buffoon who just didn't know when he was in the water over his head.

But gradually it began to dawn on his roommates that Andy was not quite so dull as he seemed. When he got his teeth into a problem, Andy didn't let go until it was solved. He picked up new ideas slowly, but when he mastered them, they were mastered once and for all. He had trouble with chemistry and biology courses, and math was especially difficult at first, but by grinding away at them doggedly, bit by bit he got them whittled down to size and kept them there.

At the same time, he began to develop some ideas of his own in his science courses and started asking questions in his slow, quiet way that nobody else even thought of asking.

Andy probably didn't earn a single A grade all through college, but when he graduated with his Bachelor of Science degree in physics he was among the three applicants out of twenty-five who were invited to stay on in the physics department of the university to work for his master's degree on a teaching fellowship.

Andy was granted his Ph.D. in physics at the age of twenty-six. He is now the assistant professor of physics at another university and is deeply involved in basic research on the nature of sub-nuclear particles, with a government contract to equip his laboratory. He is still just as slow and stolid as he ever was, but he is tenacious, and above all he has an unquenchable, burning interest in the work he is doing.

These are the personal qualities that mean the most in a career in science: a deep-seated, unshakable interest in science, an insatiable curiosity, a capacity for stubbornly hanging on through thick and thin to the end of a problem, the willingness to work hard and doggedly, and an ability to find excitement and satisfaction in the day-to-day work in the laboratory with a problem which may never ultimately yield to your study.

There is no place in science for the quitter, for the fast-talking operator without ability to back up his talk, or for the brilliant but unstable ones who can't settle down to hard work no matter how hard they try. Throughout the ages, nature has guarded her secrets with care. She will not yield them up to a superficial probe, to a casual glance, or to a few brilliant stabs in the dark. Only by careful, stubborn, tenacious digging can we hope to tear them from her. And only those with the ability to control their intelligence and make it go to work for them can do that kind of digging.

Above all else, the scientist must be fiercely interested in what he is doing. He must be interested enough to be able to survive failure after failure, and still keep on. He must be interested enough to realize that he may *never* succeed, and still be willing to spend his life trying.

The Testing Ground

I realize perfectly well that these qualities I have been talking about are not exactly easy for anyone to evaluate in himself objectively. If you have convinced yourself that a scientific career is what you want, you can very easily convince yourself that you have all of these qualifications and some extra ones for good measure, even if you really have none of them at all. Yet these are not obscure and mysterious qualities that defy identification. If you are willing to watch yourself and test yourself as honestly as possible, you can at least begin to judge where you measure up and where you fall down. Each of these qualities tends to come out in the wash at one time or another during high school and college, the testing ground of the would-be scientist.

Already you have some fairly reliable criteria for evaluating your interest in science. A check list of the books you have read in the last year or two would be a good place to start. You have already had a chance to begin your scientific training; the doors of the public and school libraries have been open to you, and those libraries contain thousands of books. If so far you have shunned the libraries or found yourself confused or bored or uninterested in the books dealing with science that you have found there, be wary. You are not likely to be any more interested in the textbooks of chemistry, physics, or biology that you will encounter in college. But if you have found yourself reading everything you can find on the shelf about certain scientific subjects, and then going out looking for more, there is hope. If you find yourself puzzling over questions raised by your reading that have not been answered to your satisfaction, the chances are that your interest will be stimulated as you move into the more complex aspects of scientific training.

It would be well to consider very carefully your own reaction to the courses in math and science you have studied in high school. A vague, passing fascination with the wonders of science is one thing; a really solid interest and spark of excitement in the workings of science is something else. You are the only one who really knows what kind of a spark, if any, those courses touched off when you took them.

For those of you who are still not certain if a career in science is really what you want or not, there are a number of ways you can test your interest before embarking on a formal training program. Most high schools and preparatory schools, in addition to science courses, have extracurricular science clubs you can join. Some such clubs are simply gatherings of students interested in carrying out science projects under the guidance of interested science teachers. Many others are member groups in the Science Clubs of America. In these gatherings, each member has an opportunity to explore various fields of science.

Many schools sponsor local science fairs, featuring exhibits prepared by interested students. Each year the Science Clubs of America sponsor a National Science Fair in co-operation with dozens of local community science fairs. These science fairs provide an incentive for young people interested in science to put their interests to work in specific projects which can be presented as exhibits.

Still another national science activity open to high school

seniors is the annual Science Talent Search, again conducted by Science Clubs of America and sponsored by the
Westinghouse Educational Foundation for the purpose of
promoting education and interest in science. The Science
Talent Search is actually a nationwide scholarship competition, with four-year scholarships awarded to the winners.
But more than that, it provides any high school senior an
opportunity to test his abilities and interests in the field.
To enter, you must undertake a science project and carry
it through, doing the necessary background reading, con-
ducting your own experiments, and writing a brief report
of your results. There is no better way to discover first-hand
the fun and excitement of scientific work, if your interest
in science is genuine. Further information about the Science
Talent Search, and about Science Clubs of America, can be
obtained by writing to Science Service, 1719 N Street,
N.W., Washington 6, D.C.

But you will have an even better chance to test your
interests after you have begun your basic science training in
college. Sometimes it is not possible to be sure you will
really enjoy something until you have become deeply involved in it. If you find first-year chemistry dull and first-
year physics confusing and hard to understand, you are
very likely in the wrong field of work.

But if somewhere in the sciences a spark of interest flares
up, you will know it. If you find yourself stimulated by the
ideas and problems which you encounter, and if you find
your interest quickening to the point that you want to dig
in and go to work, it may be that you have found precisely
the right place for your talents in the world of science. This
point is where your training to become a scientist has really
begun in earnest.

The chances are that it will never come to an end.

FIVE

Mathematics: The Language of Science

SO FAR IN THIS BOOK we have said very
little about specific fields in science. The scope of science is
enormous and all inclusive; the place where the scientist fits
into the world of science is at best difficult to understand
and at worst downright confusing. In the previous chapters
we have considered what science is, what its demands are,
and what its rewards may be. We have discussed the kind
of individual the scientist must be, the kind of work he does,
and a general outline of the sort of education and training
he must undergo.

But if the study of the world of nature is a vast undertaking made up of many parts, it is important to remember
that progress in science is made by individuals working in
narrowly specialized fields. The world of science is too enormous for any one man or group to try to encompass the
whole. Our knowledge of the universe and the way it works
has not been obtained by attacking the problems of the universe broadside.

On the contrary, our gains in science have been made by
individual men chipping away bit by bit at the frontier of
the unknown. One of the reasons that the earliest civilizations

made so little progress in science was simply that they were not content to start with tiny problems and try to piece together general principles a little at a time. As Sir James Jeans has pointed out, progress in science really began when a scientist selected some special phenomenon or special property of matter and singled it out for detailed experimental study, hoping that in this way law and order might be detected in one small corner of the universe. When this had been achieved, the frontier of scientific knowledge was pushed back a little and more questions were then asked of nature by means of direct experiment.

To the Greek philosophers this was a ridiculous approach. They did not want scraps of knowledge about isolated corners of the universe. They were interested in finding a final, complete, all-inclusive view of the whole. Needless to say, they did not find what they were looking for—but by nibbling away on a fragment at a time over the centuries, the scientist has actually begun to find what the Greek philosophers were seeking.

This need to divide the world of science into manageable segments is as great today as ever before. We mentioned before the need for skilled "scientific integrators" to fit the knowledge from one field into useful spots in other fields, but it is still the bare truth that the great majority of scientists will make worth-while contributions only if they concentrate and specialize to an extreme degree. In this way an individual can at least hope to add another small piece to the puzzle. If he does not do it this way, he may spend his life running about wildly trying to learn everything at once and end up learning nothing at all.

Because of this specialization, the various great fields of science are quite different from one another in many ways. It follows that the training of would-be scientists in

these fields is also somewhat different. It is not my intention
in this book to go into exhaustive detail about the special
training required and the special problems you will encounter in any one of the great fields of science—that would
require an entire book about each field.* But it may be helpful in this and the following chapters to discuss in broad
outline certain of the great fields of science and to consider
a few of their special requirements and a few of the opportunities they present to prospective scientists today. What
part of the world of nature do these fields actually deal
with, and how do they fit into the circle of science? What
special qualifications will you need to find a place in them?
What special opportunities are open to you with training
in them?

Above all, what sort of work lies on the frontier of each
of these fields?

In order to consider such questions, we could find no
better place to begin than with the great binding field of
them all, the field which some scientists maintain is not science at all and which others maintain is the only true science there is: the science of mathematics.

The Language of Science

Somewhere in the shadows of ancient history a great scientist of his time crawled out of his cave and discovered
that when he set two rocks down beside two other rocks he
always ended up with four rocks. It was a momentous discovery.

The first cave man who discovered that he could enu-
merate things by counting on his toes actually made one

* See Alan E. Nourse, *So You Want to Be a Doctor* (New York: Harper & Brothers, 1957).

of the greatest scientific breakthroughs of all time. Without his contribution, it is doubtful that the search for knowledge would ever have gotten off the ground; certainly none of the fields of science could ever have advanced beyond the most primitive levels of observation and speculation about it. And the day that cave man thought of representing his ten toes by drawing ten straight lines on the ground was the day the language of science was born.

Mathematics has been loosely defined as "the science of numbers," a process of reasoning by means of the use of symbols, but it is far more than that. In the endless search for an understanding of our universe and the way it operates, mathematics is the science which shows us how to deal with unknown quantities and how to organize their relationships into logical, comprehensible patterns. Mathematics enables us to represent such indefinable and intangible concepts as time, space, energy, and movement by symbols with which we can work.

Ever since man appeared on earth, we have been able in our minds to symbolize ideas and thoughts by sound patterns, words and letters, and thus communicate our ideas to others by means of spoken language. In the same way, mathematics provides us with a way to translate scientific concepts into symbols which can then be studied, manipulated, understood, and discussed. The symbols of mathematics are a written language. By using that language, the most abstract concepts, ideas, and relationships of science can be placed on paper, and by using the methods of reasoning made possible by mathematical symbols we are able to express what is known in science and predict the patterns that will be found in the unknown.

Of all the sciences, mathematics is the most orderly, the

most logical, and the most rigidly disciplined. It is true that the different branches of mathematics—simple arithmetic, algebra, plane, solid, and analytical geometry, differential and integral calculus, statistics, probability, theory of numbers, and so forth—may use different symbols and serve different purposes, but all adhere to the same formal, rigid principles of logic and proof.

As with any of the sciences, we can make a distinction between pure mathematics and applied mathematics. The scientist working in pure mathematics is seeking out basic truths about the relationship of mass, energy, and space in the universe, with no particular interest in how these truths may be used. The goal of pure mathematics is to find useful ways to describe space, time, mass, matter, and energy, to discover the ways they are interrelated, and to translate the natural laws governing these relationships into symbols that can be studied and manipulated. The theory behind the electronic computers, and the attempts to relate mass and energy in the great relativity theories and "unified field" theories which have shaken our modern concepts of physics and astronomy to the roots are just a few of the by-products of research in pure mathematics.

But more and more, mathematicians are being called on to use their specialized skills and techniques to help solve specific problems that need solving. Both the government and industry are using mathematicians in increasing numbers to outline the general directions that research should take to attain specific goals. If the pure mathematicians are the basic truth seekers in science, the applied mathematicians are the problem solvers, seeking out new applications for basic knowledge that is uncovered and clearing the way for the research scientists, the engineers, and the technologists.

Mathematicians Are Born, Not Made

With mathematics serving as a universal language of science, it is necessary for anyone entering any field of science to have at least a basic working acquaintance with math. How firm this acquaintance must be depends on the field of science. Physicists and chemists are working in specialized areas where a solid grounding in math is a tool of critical importance; these scientists must also be competent mathematicians. On the other hand, those working in biology and medicine may find less need for mathematics. For most scientists mathematics is only a useful tool, an adjunct to their work. No particular *talent* for mathematics is needed, only the intelligence and native ability necessary to understand the basic principles.

But for those interested in mathematics as a career, more than an average intelligence and ability are required. Anyone who hopes to achieve anything whatever in mathematics has to be good at it to start with. There is no place in this field for mediocrity. The prospective mathematician needs a high degree of natural ability with numbers and an ability to grasp the complex relationships of mathematics easily and clearly.

The student who has to sit down and plod through the processes of problem solving in algebra with one eye on the answer sheet is not going to be a good mathematician no matter how hard he tries. Neither is the one who has to work to grasp the basic concepts of differential or integral calculus. Above all, the individual whose imagination is shackled to rigid forms and rules of thinking will be hopeless as a mathematician.

In fact, the best of all possible qualifications for the would-be mathematician is a free-wheeling imagination and an enormous elasticity of mind—the ability deliberately to throw out all preconceived ideas of the right and wrong ways of attacking a problem, and a willingness to try new ways even though they do not conform to established patterns. This peculiar imaginative ability is useful to anyone in science; for the mathematician it is essential.

Anyone who plays chess can easily test his own elasticity of mind by trying a variation of the game called variable or "fairy" chess. The classical game of chess is governed by a set of rigid rules which govern the moves each piece can make on the board. Chess is a very deceptive game; the rules are so simple that an intelligent five-year-old can learn them, yet the game is in fact one of the most complex and difficult ever invented.

In fairy chess the players arbitrarily alter one or another of the moves of the men for the purpose of a single game, thus adding a new variable to the rigid rules. For example, you might decide that any pawn on the board can move either one or two spaces forward at any time in the game, rather than just on its first move, and then play the game according to this altered rule.

A little experimenting will show you that even such a simple change as that alters the game profoundly. It is as if you were suddenly playing an entirely different and far more complex game. Many people who try fairy chess become so hopelessly confused by it that they cannot play at all, and these are the ones whose minds are rigidly bound down by the rules, unable to stretch their minds to encompass something new, different, or unexpected. The ones who adjust easily to the variables of fairy chess are the ones whose minds are elastic, able to handle changes without difficulty. And these, more likely than not, are the ones with natural mathematical ability.

You can judge your own natural ability in math simply by your response to math courses you have already taken. To some students algebra and geometry have been dreary experiences; to others they have proven challenging and exciting. Most students can master high school algebra if they work hard enough—but there is a significant difference between those who find it fun and those who merely grit their teeth and put up with it.

You may not be able to decide whether or not mathematics is the field you want to work in until you have gotten well started in your undergraduate college work. In some ways, having made no final decision may be good, because your mind will be more open to other scientific fields. The work in math that you will do in the first years of college will stand you in good stead anywhere in science, and if you have natural mathematical ability it will have a chance to make itself known before you are committed.

Training in Mathematics

During the four years of undergraduate college, the prospective mathematician will find his work much the same as that of any other student working for a bachelor's degree in science.

As we discussed before, these four years of college are spent building a basic groundwork in science. Their purpose is to teach scientific method and imaginative thinking and to instill the habits and discipline of thinking which you will need, whether you go on for advanced work in graduate school or directly into industry or some other form of scientific work after graduation from college.

In math, as in any other branch of science, your studies will acquaint you with a great deal that has already been discovered and will teach you the tools and techniques you will need to put that knowledge to work in the search for more.

As a math major, of course, you will have more formal courses in math than most other science majors. A certain minimum work in math will be prescribed; above that there are no rigid requirements, and you will be free to elect various math courses or not, as you wish. But at the very least you will be taking 3 semester hours of math each term, or 6 semester hours per year, totaling a minimum of 24 credit hours of math out of the 120 credit hours required for a degree.

Most math majors take considerably more math than this minimum of one hour out of five. Those of you who find a real spark of interest and excitement in math will be eager to get as much math as your college has to offer, and too often the tendency is to try to take math courses to the exclusion of anything else in college.

Characteristically, you will start work in your major field slowly. Your freshman courses in math may be little more than reviews of the basic principles of algebra, geometry, and calculus which you have perhaps already studied in high school. In many colleges mathematics majors are given placement examinations in basic understanding of mathematical techniques, in order to determine what level of training and understanding each student has already achieved. In a field where so much depends upon individual ability and talent, such placement examinations are excellent. Too many colleges have lost highly promising prospective mathematicians to other fields through sheer boredom, by forcing them to sit through basic work they have long since mastered—or discouraged others at the outset by starting them in advanced courses without the proper background preparation.

But wherever you start, your courses in math in the second and third years will become more difficult and specialized, and the size of the classes smaller. Your freshman math courses may have been shared by dozens of premedical students, or chemistry and physics majors; your upperclass courses will have few of these interlopers to spoil the fun, and there will be no holds barred. Actually, if you have the ability to handle it, you may find yourself doing far more advanced work in your field in undergraduate school than any other kind of science major. There is a less clear-cut distinction between undergraduate and graduate work in math than in other fields of science, again because of the peculiar importance of individual ability. In most colleges, if you show promise in math, your professors will be inclined to give you the reins and allow you to take off at whatever speed and in whatever direction you find most suitable as long as you fulfill the basic requirements of your courses and satisfactorily pass the course examinations. Certainly none of them will try to hold you back, and if you are doing an advanced-degree level of work in undergraduate school you will find no shortage of help and encouragement from your instructors.

Much of the formal work in undergraduate courses involves learning techniques of problem solving. No matter how difficult the problem you succeed in solving, or how difficult the technique that you succeed in mastering, there are always more difficult problems and more complex techniques waiting for you. How much or how little effort you must expend in mastering this sort of course work depends to a large extent on your natural mathematical ability, and you have an excellent chance here to evaluate your own aptitude for the work.

You will doubtless hear a great deal said about the importance of your choice of school and of the professional stature of your professors, but in undergraduate school these things need not concern you too much. Virtually any college or university that offers an accredited degree course in mathematics will be presenting you the same things at the undergraduate level. In fact, it might be wiser to select a college that is renowned for something far removed from mathematics—perhaps for its history department, or the quality of its instruction in English literature—if you know from the beginning that mathematics is the field you most want to work in. This is really not such a frivolous suggestion as it may seem; as we will see in a later chapter, every scientist and especially the mathematician is in danger of falling into a trap of ultra-specialization to such a degree that all other interests are eclipsed entirely. There will be time enough in graduate school to concentrate one hundred per cent of your attention on your scientific problems. In undergraduate school a strong minor interest in an utterly nonscientific field will help to give your total education some much-needed balance.

The Graduate Mathematician

If, as we have seen, mathematics is the field of science which requires the greatest native ability, and perhaps requires the most of the student preparing for a career as a mathematician, what are the opportunities the field offers to the graduate mathematician when he has finished his college training in math?

Twenty-five years ago the answer to this question might have seemed fairly discouraging. Opportunities for careers in mathematics in those days were narrow indeed. Advanced study for higher degrees in pure math seemed to have little practical justification; it was reserved for a relative few exceedingly intense young scientists who because of their concern for "far out" and incomprehensible matters contributed more than their share to the popular image of the mad scientist. There was comparatively little place then for the applied mathematician, and it was not the sort of work to stimulate the imagination very much.

But the Second World War, with the blossoming of scientific development that it brought about, changed all this. Today the opportunities for the professionally trained mathematician are practically unlimited. No other field of science can offer more variety of exciting work on the very frontier of discovery.

The fact is that in the past generation the mathematician has been "discovered." He, of course, has always known that he had much to offer, if people would only listen to him. But only recently have others begun to realize what the mathematician can do, and how much time, money, and disappointment he can save workers in every other field of science. In applied mathematics, the trained mathematician today is actually the key man in multitudes of industries and thousands of new developmental projects. In theoretical math he is working on the frontier of a vast and exciting era of discovery—discovery that is completely shattering and reshaping our views of the structure and nature of the universe.

The graduate mathematician today will have no trouble finding a job to suit his abilities and his tastes. Rather, his major problem will be choosing between the multitudes of opportunities that are open to him.

There are still relatively few who go on for advanced math degrees, in comparison to other fields of science. For those who do, advanced training is even more of an individual tutoring and guidance program than in most fields.

Much depends on the quality of the guidance; the student with enough drive and ability to do advanced work in math would do well to seek out his professor with care, and go to the places where the really outstanding work in math is being done, to carry on his training.

The majority of graduate mathematicians seek positions in academic life, government, or industry that will allow them to put their training to practical use. Many enter teaching, from high school level on up. Still more find places where their training can be applied to the problems of modern scientific work.

The applied mathematician of today is more than just a problem solver. He is in fact the "pivot man" in many major scientific developments and projects. When a new project is contemplated, whether it be the guidance system for an intercontinental missile, a new form of high-stress construction material, or a permanent manned satellite station to orbit the earth, the mathematician is the first man who is consulted on the project, and often he is the man who can make it or break it. He is expected to determine whether the project is theoretically possible in the first place or not. He is asked to set up the basic limits within which the project can be built, to draw the rough outline plan of what sort of thing is theoretically possible that can still perform the desired functions. Once the project is on the drawing board, the mathematician is consulted constantly at every step of the way with regard to the project's structure and function.

There was a time when this kind of question was answered mainly by trial and error. A given machine or instrument needed to do a certain thing was built in prototype and then rebuilt and rebuilt again until the bugs were ironed out. Now the mathematician can predict the bugs before they appear and show the engineers how to build the machine without the bugs in the first place. It is impossible to estimate the time, money, and work that applied mathematicians in industry have saved their companies, and it is no surprise that the industries involved in the development of advanced scientific projects are constantly on the search for imaginative mathematicians and are willing to pay them excellent salaries for their services. The more advanced the mathematician's training and skill, and the more imaginative his work, the more he can expect in salary and the more important the position and responsibility he can assume.

There are other places where applied mathematics has its place. Without the work of actuaries the life insurance and other insurance companies simply could not function. The actuary determines the probabilities of loss in any form of insurance and calculates the necessary cost of the insurance for the kind of coverage it provides. Often this strikes students as rather uninspiring work, yet for the individual who wants to use his mathematical education in a steady position that has virtually no limit on income and advancement, actuarial work offers an ever-increasing opportunity.

But with the "discovery" of the mathematician, even theoretical mathematicians have found new opportunities for them appearing in industry. The days when these scientists were strictly ivory-tower thinkers, teaching mathematics in the universities, and thinking long imponderable thoughts in their research labs is gone. There is still a need for just such professional mathematicians, and much of the theoretical work in math is being done in just that way, but more and more industries are discovering that it is worth while to have mathematicians working in pure math and mathematical theory under their aegis without restricting

the angles of approach to their work or insisting upon
week-by-week returns on their investments. Some industries,
in fact, have no choice in the matter!

One of the most excellent examples of this curious state
of affairs can be seen in the problem facing the manufacturers of electronic calculators and computing instruments.
These companies are busy building immensely complicated
machines, with new refinements being devised so fast that the
working models are obsolete almost as fast as they come out
of production, and sometimes before. The companies making these machines are naturally eager to find new uses for
them, new ways they can be put to work by the people or
firms that buy them.

But the manufacturers of the great electronic computers
have come up against an apparently ridiculous problem:
they don't know for sure what their own machines can do!
Many of these computers are so complex that nobody is certain what their limitations are or what unsuspected jobs
they might be able to do. These companies have been hiring
theoretical mathematicians, not to settle down to work on
specific applied problems, but simply to study the theory
of the machines that the companies have made, to learn anything they can learn about them and what they can be made
to do. This kind of research in cybernetics, computer mechanics, or computer programming branches off in a thousand
different directions with no specific goals at all—yet these
mathematicians are paid high salaries to carry on this kind
of unfettered, no-holds-barred research.

The companies that make these machines have learned
what many other industries are learning: that money spent
to support basic scientific research is likely to pay off far
more than that spent on restricted, practical, pin-point research programs. A mathematician might draw a fifteen

thousand dollar salary for twenty years end-running without turning up a single item of value to his employer—yet if just once in that twenty years he discovers a single completely new and previously unsuspected way to put a computer to work, that knowledge could be worth a fortune to his company. This is a straightforward gamble, and such companies by nature do not like to gamble; yet they are discovering that this is the kind of a gamble that they cannot afford to refuse.

After all, it is only through pure research in science that new basic ideas are developed, and if all of our scientific talent is channeled into a search for practical applications for the basic knowledge we already have, we are heading down a blind alley. The only way out is the search for expanded knowledge and new basic understanding of nature. In this coming half-century we will almost certainly see industry competing fiercely with the academic institutions for the talents of the most promising researchers in pure science as well as in applied science.

In both applied and theoretical mathematics much the same opportunities exist on different levels for those with bachelor's degrees and for those with advanced degrees. Most often those who go ahead for advanced degrees or intend to enter into academic life are the ones who intend to spend their time in pure mathematical research. But many opportunities exist for those with less specialized training, depending more on their abilities than on their college degrees.

There are even multitudes of opportunities for those who have never taken a degree in mathematics but have a distinct mathematical aptitude. Every scientific laboratory has use for individuals with any degree of mathematical training; many excellent applied mathematicians in industry today, drawing good salaries and working on exciting projects, have degrees not in mathematics, but in engineering or physics or one of the other scientific fields. They simply happen to have the mathematical ability needed on their particular projects. At any level of scientific work a background in math will be useful, whether in pure research, in applied mathematics, in actuarial work, in statistical analysis, or any other place.

But there is no field in science that presents a more exciting frontier to a young would-be scientist. The full potentials of the electronic computers have not even been approached; we are poised on the brink of a great revolution in our way of life as a result of these complex electronic machines. Some gloomy ones complain that these machines will take over the world from human beings, but this is foolishness—these machines do not think, but simply do the drab, uninteresting, hard-labor type of work that releases human beings to do creative work they could not do otherwise. Without the mathematicians to guide them, these machines are helpless.

And the frontier extends into many other areas, too: into astronomy, into cosmology and the theory of the origin and destination of our universe, into the nature of time and space and the relationships between them, into aeronautics and astronautics, and all of the aspects of the forthcoming exploration of space.

In each of these fields the pivot man, the man in the forefront, will be the mathematician. His skill with the language of science will to a large extent determine how far scientific endeavor will progress in the next century.

SIX

The Physical Sciences: Chemistry and Physics

BUT MATHEMATICS IS BY NO MEANS the only scientific frontier in our modern world. After picking up speed over the centuries, practically every field in the world of science has reached a point now where it is falling over itself in its progress. With the vast new horizons that have been opening up in recent years, there is no field of science that will not witness enormous progress and exciting discoveries within our lifetime, and this progress will be the most impressive in the fields of the physical sciences.

Most of the practical results of scientific discovery that we see in the world around us today have resulted from the exploration, description, and understanding of our physical world. The physical sciences are concerned with the minute building blocks that make up our universe and with the ways these building blocks interact to form the substances which we use in our everyday life. These sciences are concerned with the nature of matter and the way it reacts with itself, and with the kinds of energy that lie trapped in the matter that makes up the universe. The two great subdivisions of the physical sciences—physics and chemistry—work side by side to expand our knowledge of matter and energy and how to control them. It is largely the knowledge that has been accumulated in these two fields that has revolutionized our world and given us control over our environment such as man has never had before.

In physics we have learned to understand a great deal about the basic building blocks of matter: the atoms and the subatomic particles and forces that make up the atoms, the protons and neutrons that form the nuclei of these building blocks, and the electrons that provide their means of stability. In physics we have begun to understand the natural laws governing the behavior of electrons and the phenomena of electricity and radioactivity.

We have also learned a great deal about the great mass relationships of the planets and the stars, and about the nature of the forces and the energies that move them. We have explored the phenomenon of light and learned much about its nature and the speed of its travel; we have learned about sound and discovered that the dreadful "sound barrier" that was once thought to be impenetrable really wasn't after all. We have studied the dynamics of rocket engines and have developed new means of looking far out into space with instruments immensely more sensitive than the human eye. We have opened the door to an enormous source of energy and power in the atomic structure of matter, with an understanding of the basic relationship between mass and energy, and the discovery that the physical mass of atoms can actually be converted into energy under controlled conditions. We have found ways of producing such energy from atomic sources that could power the world from now to the end of time.

And through an "unholy alliance" of mathematics and physics we have also developed the kind of power that could wipe every trace of life off our planet in one catastrophic blow. If the discoveries of the physicist seem almost unbelievable, the responsibility he has also placed in the hands of mankind is unbelievably great.

But if the physicist has unearthed some of the great natural laws that have changed our lives and will change them even more in the future, the chemist has been almost as influential in shaping the world that we live in. The chemist is concerned with the way in which the building blocks of the universe join together to form substances and react with each other to form other substances. These substances—the molecules and molecular chains which compose the materials we use for food, clothing, shelter, and medicines are the products of the chemist. They are also the substances of life. The chemist is interested in the resins and plastics which have been put to a million uses in the modern world, but he is also concerned with the enzyme systems, the proteins, fats, carbohydrates, and nucleic acids which make up the substance of living tissue itself. The chemist studies the way these substances interact in the chains of reaction which are the basic processes of life. He is concerned with forces required to bring about these chains of reaction and with the kinds of energy that they produce.

There is an area where the distinction between chemistry and biology becomes extremely fuzzy. The study of the chemistry of life processes, known as biochemistry, belongs as much to the life sciences as it does to the physical sciences, just as the lines of distinction between the physical sciences and the earth sciences become indistinct in such fields as astronomy and meteorology. We must remember that the dividing lines are frankly artificial, set up only as a matter of convenience in discussing broad general areas of scientific work. The chemist may be involved with the physics of chemistry or with the chemistry of life, either one. He is none the less a chemist.

The Bodies in the Laboratory

Some years before the death of the famous mathematician of Princeton, New Jersey, a group of fraternity pledges from an eastern college were ordered as a hazing stunt to "go to the place where Einstein thinks" and obtain an interview with the great man. The wording of their instructions was singularly appropriate. Certainly that man's contribution to the world of science was the result of his enormous thinking ability, and it was common knowledge that Einstein's intellectual preoccupation with his work was so great that he often tended to ignore the ordinary comforts and necessities of life.

Every field of science has its genius-level thinkers, the brilliant men who spend their time far more profitably in reflection and thinking than at the blackboard or in the laboratory. Nevertheless, the great bulk of valuable scientific research is still accomplished in the experimental laboratory, whether the working tools be blackboard and chalk, or billion-electron-volt generators.

Your scientific training in physics or chemistry will differ from training in mathematics more in the emphasis upon experimentation and laboratory work than in any other way. In any college or university in the country, long after the English majors and history majors have gone home to supper, the "bodies in the laboratory" are still hard at work, finishing up the experiments that were started hours before. The physical sciences are laboratory sciences and much of your formal training in these sciences will be devoted to learning the use of the laboratory tools and laboratory methods which will become your stock in trade.

Likewise, there is far more emphasis upon scientific method and learning by experiment in chemistry or physics than in mathematics. From the beginning of your college work you will be studying the work that has been done before; by the process of repeating many of the basic experiments, seeing how they were devised, and seeing how the scientific method was applied to them, you yourself will learn what must be learned and how to learn more.

In your undergraduate work your training will follow closely prescribed lines in the first three years, both in laboratory science requirements and in certain nonscientific courses. Whether your interest lies in physics or in chemistry, you will have basic English requirements and at least one foreign language requirement to fulfill in almost any college or university offering a degree course. You will be expected to take at least one year of math, which in many schools is a general survey course of many of the basic mathematical techniques rather than an intensive course in any one field of math. You will be free to elect other liberal arts courses, such as history, English literature, or philosophy, all designed to build a background against the time when you will be devoting your full time and effort to scientific pursuits.

In science courses, the work of the physics major and the chemistry major will be similar in many ways, too, and both will cross over to some extent into the other's field. Thus the would-be physicist will find himself taking at least one course in chemistry, and the prospective chemist will be studying the basic principles of physics. In either field you will follow an orderly program of courses to introduce you

to new ideas, new concepts, and new methods in a manner
that allows you to use what you have already learned in
understanding what is coming next.

The Program in Chemistry

Often the chemistry major's first college contact with his
field is disappointing. If he has studied any chemistry in
high school, the introductory lectures in inorganic chemistry
may seem to be covering old ground.

Inorganic chemistry deals with the basic principles of
chemical reactions among some of the more simple chemical
substances. In lectures and in the laboratory the elements
themselves and their properties are studied, with the major
compounds that they form, their relationships one to another, and the laws that govern their interactions. The apparent simplicity of inorganic chemistry can fool you; here,
just as in chess, it is possible to learn the simple rudiments
of the game very easily and go through the motions of playing, only to discover later some of the fascinating and exciting complexities the game has to offer. Many of the
fundamental concepts of inorganic chemistry seem ridicu-
lously simple until you begin to see how they fit into a far
more complex pattern.

For instance, in inorganic chemistry you will make your
first acquaintance with the table of the elements which was
devised in the nineteenth century by the Russian chemist
Mendelyeev. At first glance this table appears to be a simple
method of classifying the various elements according to their
molecular weights and their electron rings. The Mendelyeev
table makes a very pretty and impressive wall decoration when
it is printed up in colors, and it may be seen hanging in
practically any first-year chemistry laboratory. It is only
when you become acquainted with this table and some of its

not-so-simple implications that you begin to realize the profound importance of this classification of the elements, with the amazingly accurate predictions about previously unknown elements that it made possible. It is no accident that the science fiction writers who have tried to envision alien life forms have so often speculated upon silicon-based life, or possibility of a life form using sulfur vapor rather than oxygen in its respiratory system. The similarities between silicon and carbon, and between sulfur and oxygen were pointed out by Mendelyeev.

Here you will learn the basic laboratory tools that the chemist has to use, and encounter the basic principles of experimental method. You will learn the kinds of mathematical calculations that are helpful in predicting the course of chemical reactions and in analyzing the reactions you observe.

But inorganic chemistry is just a start. As a prospective chemist you will move step by step into courses in analytical chemistry—*qualitative analysis*, a means of determining what chemical components are present in a given substance, and *quantitative analysis*, concerned with determining how much of a given component is present. In these courses you learn more specialized laboratory methods and at the same time become acquainted with the more complex principles of ionization, thermodynamics, and acid-base balance.

It is in analytical chemistry that you first encounter some of the more startling concepts of chemistry that are not commonly recognized. It is here also that you begin the process of unlearning many things you have learned before and learning them over again correctly. For example, you may have learned in high school chemistry that substances were either soluble in water or insoluble in water. This is a nice, clean-cut idea which is easily understood and useful—but unfortunately not quite true. You will learn instead that a universal solvent such as water will dissolve a certain amount of virtually *any* substance, no matter how "insoluble" it may be, and that even the most minute quantities of these substances dissolved in water can be extremely significant when one is talking about the life or death of living tissue.

But for the would-be chemist, the most important single course in chemistry is one which is usually met in the third year of college: the study of the chemistry of carbon compounds, known as *organic chemistry*.

In this course, the truly complex nature of the world of chemistry begins to appear. The puzzling concepts of inorganic and analytical chemistry seem wonderfully clear in comparison to the almost unbelievably complicated tangle that one encounters in organic chemistry. Probably the most difficult single course that any college has to offer, organic chemistry is the real test course for the would-be chemist. If he can unravel the many twisting threads of this branch of chemistry, enjoy it, understand it, and master it, he will have no difficulty in establishing his career in chemistry. If he finds organic chemistry too difficult, too dull, or just plain incomprehensible, the chances are that he will end up finding his work in another field. Very few students find this branch of chemistry easy to understand at first, but as in any other area of science there is a clear, logical pattern to it, and an understanding of organic chemistry is the basis for the greatest bulk of the work being done in chemistry today.

Awaiting those who survive organic chemistry is physical chemistry. This branch of chemistry deals with the energy relationships of chemical reactions, with the intricate balance between acids and bases in solutions, and with the chemistry of atomic nuclei. Physical chemistry lies on the dividing line between physics and chemistry, one of the places where the would-be chemist steps completely over the line to study the basic principles of physics.

The Program in Physics

As you may have gathered by now, the physics majors and the chemistry majors are really brothers under the skin. Their programs of training in college are similar, and many classes are in fact shared. These two great fields of the physical sciences are concerned with different aspects of the same thing, and the fields interlock at a dozen different points.

The main difference in the physicist's training is in emphasis. He will be taking basic chemistry courses—and often organic chemistry, too—but he will spend much more time in mathematics than in chemistry. Like the chemist, the physicist will follow a step-by-step introduction to progressively more difficult ideas, but the various courses he will take in physics are not separate studies. Each will add a bit more to his overall concept of the energies and driving forces that operate in the universe.

Once again, in the basic courses in physics the prospective physicist will at first be concerned with rather commonplace things that are familiar to everyone. Here you will study the basic principles of mechanics and mechanical forces, of electricity and electromagnetic forces, and of atomic structure and the forces of radioactivity. Other physical phenomena are literally "taken apart" to see what makes them function, among them the phenomena of sound, light, and heat. You will study the development of some of the great natural laws of the universe—conservation of energy and matter, gravitation, and relativity.

Against this general background you will move into more

detailed study of various aspects of physics. As in chemistry you will encounter a number of startling and not at all commonly recognized concepts—for example, the critical question of whether light occurs in waves with certain of the properties of particles, or as particles with certain of the properties of waves; and the modern evidence that basic components of atoms, such as electrons, may not be solid particles at all but merely compact bundles of energy that behave somewhat like solid particles. You will study the structure of atoms and the nature of radiation, nuclear energy, and cosmic rays.

Just as in chemistry, your work in physics goes from the simple to the complex. It also grows progressively more interesting as you leave the commonplace ideas behind and become involved in more complicated and stimulating aspects of physics. No one will ever know how many fine potential physicists have been bored out of physics by the commonplace material and the dull presentation of basic physics courses; more and more attempts are being made to present the "simple" principles of mechanics and electricity in such a way as to draw the student to physics rather than drive him away.

Your training in physics will depend a great deal more on laboratory experience than on lectures or reading at home. Most courses in physics involve a few hours of lecture per week, but they also involve long afternoons spent in the laboratory. These are time-consuming courses; when you have two or three of these in a year back to back, plus your other courses, you have far less time to yourself for study or for social life than liberal arts majors. You may have difficulty carrying much of a load of outside work to help pay college bills. At the same time, it is a great temptation to spend all of your time in the scientific courses and to ignore other required courses altogether. This can be a dangerous trap to fall into; many a promising chemist or physicist has failed to reach his goal, not because of any failing in his chosen field, but because he failed to maintain the necessary level of work in the nonscientific courses required to obtain his degree.

Opportunities in Physics and Chemistry

By far the bulk of the graduates in physics and chemistry will seek out jobs in their respective fields after graduation from college with the bachelor's degree. The opportunities for such work are almost limitless. But most undergraduate work in these fields has been concerned just with catching up to the present, learning what has already been learned, studying laboratory techniques and working methods that are already established. Original or creative work is seldom required of an undergraduate, although students who are eager to start such work can often find encouragement and even laboratory space to do it if they wish.

In general, however, it is only in graduate training, working toward master's and doctoral degrees, that the would-be scientist encounters the advanced problems and discovers the truly creative part of scientific work. Many students who do well in undergraduate work and have hopes and ambitions to do original research will at least begin on the road toward an advanced degree, if it is possible.

But whether you decide to begin work in physics or chemistry with a bachelor's degree or elect to go on first for an advanced degree, there are few other fields of science which could offer you a wider variety of opportunities. In the last few decades, new vistas have opened up in every field of science, and there is every indication that this enormous expansion will continue in the next fifty years, gaining speed all the way. Virtually *any* trained scientist will be able to find a place in this expansion.

But the physicists and chemists, above all, are destined to be the world-shapers of the future.

A whole book could be written dealing just with the opportunities that now exist for men and women trained in chemistry and physics without even touching on the remarkable possibilities for the future which are just beginning to appear. There was a time when the world could take scientific discoveries or leave them alone; that time is long since passed. Today the world is depending upon basic research in chemistry and physics to open the way to greater and greater control of the forces of nature which govern the way people can live.

We depend upon the new generation of chemists and physicists to find ways to use this basic knowledge to provide us with the new materials, products, and techniques which we will be using in the next hundred years. Much of the speculative fiction that has been written in recent years has dealt with results of the work of physicists and chemists, and it is no wonder. They have made possible such things as the almost limitless sources of power from atomic energy; the electronic instruments and devices such as television and the transistor that have become commonplace in our lives; a whole new world of structural materials in the plastics, with more versatility than any other type of construction material ever discovered by man; a new and amazing variety of fibers and fabrics; and a vast revolution in the discovery and manufacture of medications and antibiotics.

Many of these advances have been the work of applied physicists and applied chemists, with the pure researchers staying a bare step ahead of them, opening up new fields of knowledge that will lead to new products and uses. Every major industry in the country, from the automobile and aircraft-makers to the manufacturers of pencil erasers, have profited from the work of applied scientists in chemistry and physics.

And many large industries maintain their own laboratories for research and development. Some companies, such as American Telephone and Telegraph, Westinghouse Electric Corporation, E. I. duPont, American Cyanamid, and other great scientific industrial concerns, have a major part of their future invested in the hands of their physicists and chemists, working today to develop the products of tomorrow.

In modern times the federal government has become a major contractor for scientific talent, supporting both basic and applied research in a wide variety of fields. Unquestionably this interest of our government in scientific development will grow larger, not smaller, as time goes on. The need for more scientists to work either in government laboratories or on government grants will be increasing year by year. It is no secret that our nation is engaged in a deadly race against time with other great nations which threaten to bury us by getting there first with the most in terms of scientific research and development. Those with faith in our tradition of free enterprise believe that we will win this race in the long run, but it will not be won by sitting on our hands.

And the front line of attack in this race is composed of scientists trained in physics and chemistry.

These sciences, like mathematics, are chipping away at the very frontier of human knowledge. Many questions have been answered; we now understand to some degree how our universe is built and how it functions—yet the knowledge that we have today represents only a tiny fraction of the total knowledge that can and will be accumulated.

One of the most exciting features of pure research in chemistry and physics is that we cannot even guess in what directions and in what areas the major breakthroughs of the next half-century will come. Scientists in these fields are trained observers, ready to recognize the significance of any phenomena that occur in the course of their experimental work, whether those phenomena happen to fit in with the work that they are doing or not. Horace Walpole's famous tale of the three princes of Serendib who traveled in quest of things which they never succeeded in finding, but discovered along the way many things which turned out to be far better than the things that they were looking for, was never more apropos than today. More often than not it is the curious and unexpected "side effect" in a series of experiments that opens the door to more important discovery than the planned experiments. Some scientists go so far as to believe that this principle of *serendipity*—the phenomenon of the "accidental discovery" which is made in the process of following up some other line of study—is the single greatest and most important source of scientific advancement. But this principle only operates when a trained, alert, elastic, scientific mind is on hand to recognize the significance of an unexpected side effect when it occurs.

We will live to see atomic energy converted to normal power uses and provide vast improvement in transportation and communication. We will see new kinds of plastics and fabrics, new forms of lighting, new ways of using and developing color, and powerful new antibiotics and other drugs. We will live to see the first major steps in the exploration of our solar system. In the midst of all these advances we will find the physicist and the chemist working individually or hand in hand. And anyone entering into these fields may be the one responsible for the major breakthroughs of the next half-century.

But you would not be wise to start off in your training in physics or chemistry with the idea of seeking only the major breakthroughs. Much more likely your work will involve the minor breakthroughs, the smaller, less dramatic advances that every scientist achieves at one time or another in his laboratory. There are comparatively few Nobel prize winners in the world, and if the major breakthroughs are the ones that capture the newspaper headlines, it is good to remember that it is not so much the brilliant flare of the genius-level scientist, but the steady chipping away at the frontier of knowledge by the "ordinary" scientist that builds the solid groundwork for progress in the future.

SEVEN

The Biological Sciences

YOU MIGHT EXPECT that anyone writing a book about science and the various scientific fields would be likely to wax more enthusiastic about his own particular field of interest than about any of the others. In writing such a book as this, the author is bound to have an axe to grind. To him the other fields of science may be entirely legitimate, interesting, even awe-inspiring in their scope and opportunities, but they just do not hold for him the same excitement and fascination of his own "home ground." No matter how hard he may try to be objective and unbiased in presenting the various fields of science, he cannot keep his own personal spark of enthusiasm out of his writing about his own favorite field.

So you will just have to bear with me when I write about the second of the great areas of scientific endeavor: the biological sciences or "sciences of life."

At least you can be thankful that I am a physician and not a geneticist, or an invertebrate zoologist, or a renal physiologist. If I were, you could expect a far worse indoctrination than you are going to get. A doctor is not usually a specialist in any particular single aspect of the life sciences; yet by the nature of his work he is vitally interested in almost all kinds of work in the life sciences at more specialized levels. More than anyone else, perhaps, he feels the vitality of this branch of science. He recognizes the significance of the work in these fields because he is working in the place where their advances are applied.

In a sense the biological sciences are physical sciences, too. They are concerned with the behavior of matter and energy in the universe, but they are especially concerned with a very specialized form of matter with certain unique characteristics. The biological sciences deal with the structure and function of living organisms of all sorts, from the lowliest single-celled water plant to the highly organized and complex organism known as the human being.

Precisely what constitutes the fine dividing line between life and non-life remains one of the great unsolved mysteries. No matter how one attempts to define what life is, one finds exceptions that do not fit the definition; the nature of the vital spark has never been understood. We have some fairly acceptable ideas about when and where and under what conditions life first appeared on earth, and we study in minute detail the various vital processes that constitute life in living organisms, but we cannot define life itself. All we know is that under certain circumstances a chain of reactions and processes occur in an orderly fashion. While that chain remains unbroken, life is present; if somewhere along the line that chain of reactions breaks down, life is no longer present even though the chemical and biological composition of the organism seems totally unchanged.

It is not until we stop to consider how subtle and complex this chain of reactions must be that we begin to recognize what a remarkable phenomenon life actually is.

I once happened to observe one of the curious differences between life and death—an observation which did not make any particular sense at the time and still remains one tiny isolated chunk of information that has never been fitted into the pattern. A physiologist friend had been studying the nature of blood-clotting mechanisms in living creatures, particularly the part that blood platelets played in the clotting of blood when it had been released from a blood vessel. Certain kinds of platelets seemed to be "sticky" and tended to break up when rubbed against a rough surface of any kind, releasing substances that furthered blood clotting. My friend had been wondering why these "sticky platelets" didn't break up inside blood vessels as they were tumbled around. He had decided that the reason might be that the inner surfaces of blood vessels in living creatures were "non-wettable" surfaces, so that blood passed over them as water passes over an oiled glass plate without wetting the surface.

In support of this idea my friend had noticed that when the stream of blood in tiny capillaries in a rabbit's ear was interrupted by pressure, the broken column of blood in the capillary did not form a meniscus, or concave upper surface, the way it would if the capillary surface was "wettable." He was showing me this curiosity in the ear capillaries of a poor unsuspecting rabbit one evening when the rabbit suddenly expired for cause or causes unknown.

Within twenty seconds after the rabbit's death, we saw the broken blood column in the capillary slowly form a tiny curved meniscus that had not been there when the rabbit was alive.

The conclusion seemed obvious: that while the creature was alive the insides of its blood vessels were non-wettable surfaces to which the blood could not attach itself. But the moment the rabbit died, a change took place in the blood vessel lining, turning it into a wettable surface. The only difference in the rabbit that we could observe was one moment it was alive and the next it was not—we had merely observed one of the many unsuspected changes that took place the moment that life was no longer present.

Men have been more vitally concerned with the problems of life—what it is, how it came about, what makes it stop, and how it may be prolonged—than any other question about our physical world. This is not surprising; after all, we are living creatures who value life, and we seek to prolong it if we can. Throughout the history of science, men have made a steady, relentless effort to understand the nature of life. And this is the work today of the biological scientist.

For many years the biological sciences were primarily concerned with description and classification. We live in a world filled with organisms of all forms and shapes and functions. For many centuries, the major work done in the life sciences was the examination of the structure of these organisms and the description of the way they functioned. Out of this kind of work the great classifications of botany and zoology appeared; the botanist concerned himself with the classification of various kinds of plant life, while the zoologist was interested in the many forms of animal life.

But gradually other questions about life began to arise. The one consistent characteristic of living organisms is their ability to reproduce in a certain fashion, with one organism giving life to a similar organism. The field of *genetics* had its birth with the work of Gregor Mendel, who first began to explore the ways in which the physical characteristics of various living organisms were handed down from generation to generation. Following in his footsteps came such great biologists as Louis Pasteur, and the idea of *experimental biology* became respectable. Life seemed to be the result of chains of chemical reactions within the bodies and cells of organisms; the study of the chemistry of life, or *biochemistry*, sought to unravel those reaction chains. The general behavior of organisms—their neurological behavior, muscular behavior, respiration, and cardiovascular function came under scrutiny, and *physiology* came into being. Other scientists began studying the effect that certain drugs could have upon living organisms, and the science of *pharmacology* had its birth. Finally, certain men began studying the changes in living organisms which caused or resulted from disease, and the science of *pathology* or "morbid anatomy" developed, leading for the first time to a scientific approach to *medicine* and the understanding and treatment of disease.

In the field of *botany*, experimental work also came into the picture, and the problems of plant reproduction, growth, physiology, and disease were studied. These investigations led to a better understanding of the plant world about us and opened up such diverse fields of discovery as *microbiology* and the development of antibiotics on one hand, and *scientific agriculture* on the other hand.

In the biological sciences more than anywhere else we are aware of the enormous advances that scientific work has brought us. We may take an indifferent attitude toward landings on the moon, and we may consider such things as television and computing machines merely as devices of the devil to further complicate an already overcomplicated life, but we cannot take an indifferent attitude toward the diseases which maim bodies and destroy life, nor toward the work which in the past ten years alone has added another seven years to the average life expectancy of every human being born today.

Describe and Draw

If you are preparing for work in any field of biological science, you will find that your training is much different from training in one of the physical sciences, even though the overall goals of training are much the same.

Where the physical sciences are concerned with natural phenomena and reactions, the life sciences are interested in chains of reaction and behavior as observed in living creatures. As a student in the biological sciences you will probably take basic courses in mathematics, chemistry, and physics, but most of your scientific training will be focused upon various aspects of the great field of biology, and it may seem in the first year or two that your laboratory work consists of little more than describing and drawing.

Whether it be in botany—the study of plant life—or zoology—the study of animal life—or embryology or bacteriology or genetics, much of your time in the laboratory will be spent examining various forms of life in various stages of development, studying their structure, testing by experimental methods their function, and putting down on paper the things you see. Sometimes this work seems discouragingly repetitive and pointless. To one who has spent many summers fishing, the earthworm may seem a rather dull and uninteresting creature to command very much attention, and I know at least one young lady in a comparative anatomy course who was more impressed with the dogfish shark as a "slimy mess," than as an excellent example of the anatomical similarity of all vertebrate animals.

But even this basic work need not be dull. Your training in the biological sciences will be designed to accomplish two purposes: to teach you an enormous fund of knowledge which has already been accumulated about the nature of life, and to teach you how to go about the further study of this life. In this field, the experimental or scientific method is now as firmly established as it is in the physical sciences, but all too often less definite conclusions can be drawn on the basis of experimental evidence than in other fields. Both physics and genetics, for instance, are logical and organized scientific disciplines, but in physics, experimental data are likely to be more conclusive. In genetics we often must limit the conclusions we draw from an experiment to the species of animal or plant involved in the experiment. Before more general conclusions can be drawn, multiple experiments with different species may be necessary.

This is just one of the reasons that the development of scientific knowledge has been slower in the biological sciences than in other fields. Traditionally, much more has been accepted on the basis of intuition and faith without proof than has been the case in the physical sciences. In a way this has been most unfortunate; it has thrown up some extremely frustrating roadblocks in the way of rational scientific investigation of the processes of life, some of which have survived persistently over the centuries in spite of all scientific efforts to tear them down.

An excellent example of such a stumbling block to scientific progress in the biological sciences was the century-long battle that raged about the phenomenon of spontaneous generation —the idea that life could spring forth spontaneously from dead matter under certain special conditions. The history of this persistent false idea is fascinating. It was supported by a multitude of excellent scientists who were perfectly well acquainted with experimental and scientific methods, but were too preoccupied with the results they wanted to obtain from their experiments to be careful to control their experiments, to close up all the gaping holes, and plug all the cracks. Again and again these men demonstrated "scientifically" that under certain special circumstances life could be generated out of dead matter in the laboratory. Even after the presence of microscopic organisms was known, and the fact proven that special broth cultures could be seeded with bacteria again even after they had been sterilized, there were certain die-hards who clung to the old traditional idea. In spite of the growing burden of scientific evidence against them, reputable scientists sought to turn the scientific method against itself to prove something which simply could not be proved scientifically because, as we now know, it just was not true.

Another reason that experimental work in the biological sciences is so complicated, and at the same time so fascinating, is the fact that hardly any experiment can be devised to observe and follow a single phenomenon. Life is a multiude of processes all going on at the same time. Almost anything that we do to influence one of these processes inevitably influences others too. Part of your training in the biological sciences is training in a rigid discipline of thinking, to help you winnow out a single phenomenon to study and to train you to devise methods to test single properties—in other words, to teach you how to control your experiments.

The species limitation we mentioned before is a hindrance in another way. In studying the effect of various diseases on men, the monkey has been a useful experimental animal because its basic structure and reactions very much resemble those of a human being. Unfortunately, we are no longer so much concerned with basic gross reactions; these have been fairly well outlined and are well understood by now. More and more we are studying the minute changes and differences

rather than the massive and obvious ones. Sometimes changes
in a single molecule in a single gene can bring about a diseased
or pathological state.

And somewhere along the line we find we can no longer draw
analogies between what is true in the monkey and what we can
assume to be true in man. Up to a certain point, for instance, a
study of the nervous system of the monkey can teach us a great
deal about the human nervous system, but beyond that point
further study will merely teach us more and more about the
nervous system of monkeys, and nothing that necessarily ap-
plies to the nervous system of human beings.

This difficulty in foreseeing the control necessary for experimental work in the biological sciences, and the great complexity of living organisms that one must be dealing with, has
led many times to false conclusions. Many a biologist has spent
his life following up an idea which appeared fruitful in early
experiments, only to discover after many years of work that
certain basic assumptions which seemed to be perfectly justi-
fied actually had no real basis in fact at all.

An excellent example of this particular pitfall appeared
several years ago in a study of diabetes mellitus, an illness in
which the body fails to produce adequate amounts of insulin
to permit the normal handling of sugar in the human body.
Until recently almost all diabetics had to take additional
amounts of insulin in order to maintain normal sugar metab-
olism. But many observers had noticed that when a diabetic
woman became pregnant, her insulin requirement often
dropped sharply as the pregnancy progressed. This phenomenon had long puzzled investigators studying the disease, and
one group set out to try to find the reason for it.

It seemed logical to assume that the mothers were getting
extra insulin from somewhere; their own bodies were not producing enough. It occurred to one investigator that the extra

insulin might be coming from the baby. As the baby grew larger, it produced more and more insulin until it was supplying the mother's requirements as well as its own.

This seemed to be a brilliant and logical idea, but how to prove it? The investigator reasoned that such a baby would still be producing enormous amounts of insulin for at least a short time after it was born. Why not test the blood sugar of such new-born babies of diabetic mothers? He began a series of tests on "diabetic" babies and discovered that their blood sugars were running at insulin-shock levels, far lower than normal adult blood sugar levels! As the babies grew older, their blood sugars began rising to approach expected levels.

The investigator immediately published the results of his work, proclaiming that babies born of diabetic mothers had abnormally high insulin-production, and were in danger of death from insulin shock unless quantities of sugar were instilled into their little stomachs immediately after birth. The discovery was hailed as a major step forward in the understanding of diabetes—until some annoying young fellow thought of testing the blood sugars of ordinary new-born babies, and found that their blood sugars also ran at insulin-shock levels, and the whole bubble burst with a resounding bang.

The investigator had certainly made a fool of himself, and his sin was a sin of omission. He had failed to establish the *normal* infant blood sugar level before testing what he thought was abnormal. Yet this kind of sin is by no means uncommon in the biological sciences. Too often the ground in these fields seems to be constantly shifting. It often is impossible really to control all of the elements you are working with. If your training in the biological sciences in college at least teaches you to be exceedingly skeptical and self-critical, and to accept nothing as true until it has been proven by other workers using the same methods of proof that you have used, it will have prepared you well, and you will have a chance of making valuable contributions in biology.

Opportunities in the Life Sciences

If those of you who are interested in the biological sciences have gathered from the public press that the hue and cry for new scientific people has focused on the physicists and chemists, you can be reassured that there will be no shortage of demand for work in your field when your training is completed.

If in no other area than in the study of the nature, treatment, and cure of human disease (and there are many other areas), the opportunities and challenges to the biological scientists of the present generation and the next generation are enormous.

After all, much of the progress made in the study and treatment of human disease in the last fifty years has been a matter of slaying a multitude of little dragons.

A look at the medical textbooks of fifty years ago shows us hundreds of diseases and conditions, then considered to be beyond the help of medical science, which are now perfectly understood and easily controlled. Tuberculosis has all but fallen by the wayside. Infectious diseases are now readily dealt with. Diabetes can be controlled now in many cases with medications taken by mouth. It seems that at every turn of the road a new disease has been conquered, a new medical problem solved.

But these have all been little dragons. There remain four giant dragons which are not by any manner of means slain, the four great killers of man: cancer, arteriosclerosis, hypertension, and old age.

The challenge facing the biological scientists who are beginning their training today is to slay these four great dragons. Each of these is a great and complex problem. Each is a ruthless killer of men. It will remain the province of the biological scientists—the physiologists, the doctors, the biochemists, the pathologists, the geneticists, the embryologists, in fact the whole phalanx of workers in the life sciences—to grapple with these killers and stop them. No war has destroyed lives more wantonly and mercilessly than cancer; no other illness has taken more lives than the heart diseases that result from arteriosclerosis and hypertension. And old age, which leads to death from the simple wearing out of the human body, remains the last enemy of man.

We have already seen in our time how a massive, concerted effort on the part of thousands of scientists can force a medical dragon to yield at last. A determined war was made on infantile paralysis, with the help of national fund raising campaigns and basic research into the nature, prevention, and cure of virus diseases. That war took years to win, but today we know that this dread disease at last can be prevented. Today the same enormous world-wide war is being made on cancer. The problem is being attacked in every conceivable way, from basic research in physiology and genetics to the opposite extreme of drug-testing in clinical medicine. So far the answer has not been found. Even the right pathways to follow have not been identified for sure. The basic clues remain obscure, yet this fearful disease will eventually buckle to the onslaught, because it is within the capability of human minds and human resources to find the way to destroy it.

But the challenges and opportunities for the biological scientist are to be found in other fields also. In the world today we face a problem of overpopulation—too many people and too little room to grow food for them. In our own country we have ample food now, but there are areas of the world where multitudes of people do not have enough to eat. It will not be too many years before our own country is hungry as well as the rest of the world, unless we can find ways to grow more and better food more rapidly.

Thus, biological scientists are already searching for ways to develop better food crops on less land. The sea presents us with an enormous challenge, and there is every possibility that the vast water areas of the earth can be turned into huge food-supplying farms for a hungry population. Conservation of other natural resources, particularly our forests, offers another challenge to the biological scientist, and the people who enter forest conservation and forestry will have no difficulty finding a place to use their talents.

Many of you with specialty training in the biological sciences will find places in industry, working with the pharmaceutical companies, for example. Others will find work supported by public funds given for specific research goals, such as the grants of the American Cancer Society, or by the great philanthropic foundations which will support any kind of research that appears promising. Many more of you will find places in academic careers with colleges and medical schools, working closely with clinical investigators and doctors. Still others will seek out medicine, either for research or for practice.

But more and more biological scientists are turning their attention to the understanding of the basic life processes, not with a specific goal in mind but simply in search of whatever can be found. We know that the four giant dragons we spoke of will not yield to the knowledge that we have accumulated so far. We have all but exhausted the knowledge that we already have; until we have a better basic understanding of the nature of life, of the nature of growth and of the biochemical reactions, the enzyme systems, and the metabolic chains that permit life to proceed, we will have little further progress and these dragons will continue to flourish.

But every new discovery, every new bit of knowledge that is uncovered opens up new avenues for discovery. There is room in this work for people trained in all levels of biological science. If we have learned nothing else in the last one hundred years, we have learned the nature of the enemy and we know that it lies within our power to conquer him.

All that is required is the workers, the imagination, and the scientific training to fight the war.

EIGHT

The Earth Sciences and Others

IN THE PREVIOUS CHAPTERS we have dis-
cussed training in mathematics, the language of science, and
two of the great fields of scientific study: the physical sciences
and the life sciences. But you will notice certain significant
gaps in the circle of science which we have not yet touched
upon. Two groups of sciences appear to lie at opposite ex-
tremes in the world of science, one of them closely allied to the
physical sciences, the other more obviously related to the life
sciences. Neither group fits neatly into either classification,
yet each has enormous importance to us in seeking a clear
understanding of our universe and the way it behaves.

These two groups of sciences are the *earth sciences*—geology, archaeology, anthropology, meteorology and astronomy
—and the *sciences of mind and behavior*—psychology, psychiatry and sociology.

If it seems to you that these two groups of scientific disciplines make uncomfortable bedfellows, perhaps you are
right. In many ways they are as different from each other as
night and day. Yet if we look closely we can find that they are
as intimately related as night and day also. Neither one makes
much sense standing alone; but each fits into place to con-

tribute a segment of knowledge to our overall understanding of the world we live in.

The Earth Sciences

Certainly scientists have undertaken a difficult and complex task in attempting to describe the physical universe and outline laws of nature that govern its behavior. Part of the difficulty is the matter of experimental materials. We can dissect an earthworm; it is more difficult to pinch an atom and observe which way it jumps than to pinch an earthworm and note how it squirms. Very often in the physical sciences we are working with substances and processes which we can identify only by very indirect methods. Our only evidence that an electron went by may be a trail of fog in a chamber or a click from a radiation detector, and we can often only guess at the molecular changes that must be taking place within a living cell when we observe the measurable changes that have occurred in the cell.

But in geology and astronomy we have the means of dissecting our universe in a very literal sense. In fact, geology and astronomy might well be considered to be the study of the "microscopic anatomy" and "gross anatomy" of the universe.

On and in the earth we have at hand the only really good specimen of a terrestrial object that has been found so far: the earth itself. The life that has appeared here has sprung up under conditions very different from the conditions of today, but it still was formed from the elements and components to be found here. It did not come here from anywhere else; it started here, built in some way out of the materials and under the conditions that existed here at one time.

It is the work of the *geologist* to study the physical nature of the earth we live on, to penetrate the mysteries of its formation, of its present structure, of its probable past structure, and of the conditions that existed here at the time that life first appeared.

It may seem odd that the work of the geologist was not done and completed long ago. After all, the earth has been here for as long as man has been here and far longer. We have had thousands of years to study it and observe what goes on with it—yet we have still barely scratched the surface, literally or figuratively.

As a youngster I was considerably baffled by my father's not-too-accurate statement that Chinamen lived on the other side of the world and walked upside down because the earth was round. This whole idea seemed very unlikely to me; anyone could see the earth was flat, and I could not see how a Chinaman could possibly hang on if he really walked upside down. At one time, to my father's chagrin, I took a shovel out to the garden, determined to dig on through and see these upside-down Chinamen with my own eyes. I had a pit ten feet deep in the cabbage patch before my father caught me, and that was the last such hole I ever dug.

But I have wondered ever since why somebody didn't just dig down and see what they could find. It is only in the last year that plans have actually been made to drill a hole down through the outer crust of the earth's surface to see what lies in the layer beneath the crust.

But the earth itself is really only exhibit A in our study of the nature of the celestial bodies. The geologist studies the composition of the earth and the changes that have come about in its crust in the last million years or so, and tries to guess the conditions that must have been present at various times to bring about the changes that he sees. But the *astronomer* works with exhibit B—the whole stellar universe that lies beyond the earth, from our own sun and the planets of our solar system to the stars that lie in such far-reaching galaxies that they cannot even be detected with the most sensitive visual telescopes or photographic plates, but can be identified only by the radio waves which emanate from them. If the geologist takes a "microscopic" look at the details of a tiny fragment of the universe, the astronomer is taking a "macroscopic" view. He is concerned with vast expanses of space and with the planetary and stellar bodies which lie unimaginable distances away. He is interested in the life cycle of stars: where they come from, how their planets form, what succession of events they must undergo in their span of existence and how they die. He is concerned with the total universe that can be detected by any means that he can find to detect it. While the geologist spends his time in the field studying the formations of rock, sampling sections of the earth's crust, and studying volcanoes and earthquakes and their effects, the astronomer is working with his extra eyes: the telescope, the photographic plate, the spectroscope, the radio-telescope, and the other devices still being developed to help him study the heavens.

Here, too, there are specialized fields of scientific work. The *archaeologist* studies the evidences that remain of civilizations and peoples of earlier times, the often scanty relics of human beings who inhabited the earth long before historical records began. From these remains he seeks to learn more about those people and about their civilizations, and to find out what has happened to the earth in the time since they were living here.

The *anthropologist* is interested in people too, both in terms of their physical development and structure and in their ways of living. He seeks to outline the changes in human form since the first men appeared on earth and to study the development of special racial characteristics. Neither of these specialized scientific fields is part of geology, yet they are certainly aligned in their fields of interest to the geologist.

Working somewhere between the geologist, the physicist, and the astronomer is the *meteorologist*, who studies the nature of our atmosphere, the changes of weather, and the conditions which affect climate in all parts of the earth. In an age when air travel is progressing rapidly and modern warfare is carried on above the surface of the ground, the meteorologist's work becomes increasingly indispensable. But his greatest challenge still lies in the future, in finding ways to control the weather that has long been considered utterly beyond man's control. The meteorologist of today is the embryonic planetary engineer of tomorrow. Vast areas of the earth are useless to man because of their frigid temperatures; other areas are tormented by consistently foul weather, and still others are barren desert. With an understanding of weather conditions and with techniques for controlling them, the planetary engineers of tomorrow could alter all three of these useless surface areas to serve us better than they can in their natural state.

On the other side of the ledger, the *cosmologist* is the astronomer concerned equally with astronomy, mathematics, and physics. The cosmologist seeks to fit the total physical structure and function of the universe, the movements of the planets and galaxies, into an orderly and predictable system of some sort. Once entirely in the realm of metaphysics and philosophy, this particular field of science still is concerned with the basic philosophical questions which have formed in men's minds since men first appeared on earth. Today we scoff and joke about the vast imponderable questions the early philosophers asked: "What is the meaning of it all? What is our place in the infinite scheme of things?" But such questions may not be so naïve and laughable after all. The cosmologist assumes an "infinite scheme of things" and searches to find our rightful place in it.

And in a larger sense, these philosophical questions are really the very same basic questions that all branches of modern science are attempting to answer. The philosophers sought to find answers through thinking, reasoning, and argument, and philosophy is still a valid way to try to find the answers. Religions seek the same answers in different ways. Science is simply another way of approaching the same core problems of our existence, a way which uses observation, measurement, and experimentation to find the answers. Cosmology as a science merely demonstrates that there is no fundamental conflict among the approaches, when the goal is the same for all.

The Sciences of Behavior

It might seem that there could be no field of science farther removed from such earth sciences as astronomy and geology than the comparatively young and budding sciences that deal with the working of the human mind, with the behavior of living creatures in general and human beings in particular.

There are still those who argue that *psychology* is not really a science at all, but merely a collection of opinions set forth by self-appointed authorities who have shouted so long and so loudly that people have begun to accept their views as true without proof. Such an attitude is a little extreme. Even though it has been extremely difficult to set up valid, controlled experiments to measure behavior patterns, in recent years psychologists have tried more and more to apply scientific methods to a kind of study which at best is highly personal and individual.

Of course, the measurements, observations, and conclusions

in psychology have never been as precise as those in physics, and probably never will be. The difference lies in the nature of the subject matter. Physics is an objective science, where the things being studied can readily be observed, measured, or counted. They hold still while you pin them down. But psychology is studying things more difficult to measure: emotions, patterns of thought, behavior patterns, reactions, and feelings. Too often such things cannot be studied objectively, and clear-cut scientific conclusions are difficult to draw.

Yet there is probably no scientific field that holds more fascination and more promise for better human relations than psychology. Even with the scanty knowledge that has already been accumulated, many of the great problems of human behavior are at least better understood. We have already gained some very useful knowledge about why people do the things they do the way they do them. Much of our knowledge in psychology and its medical sister, psychiatry, still remains theoretical but even this kind of knowledge is useful. As a science, psychology is in its infancy, but it may well grow into one of the most rewarding of scientific fields.

Preparation for a career in psychology is quite different from that in most scientific fields. Unfortunately, there is still a popular idea that psychology is a snap, that any idiot can get through training in this field. Because it deals with subjective matters which depend upon description rather than measurement, many students think of it as a field where talk is a substitute for work. Many young people with glib tongues and enough intelligence to recognize that psychology is still only incompletely a science have tried to enter the field, hoping to find an easy way to cash in their cleverness without doing too much work. For the most part these people have been sadly disappointed. They have discovered that in psychology, as in any science, there is no substitute for discipline, for an understanding of scientific methods, and for a willingness to buckle down and work hard. College psychology departments have often been too tolerant of the lazy ones and the phonies that have come their way; almost certainly as psychology develops stature as a valid science, a more rigid discipline will be needed.

Closely allied to psychology, and still an "embryonic" science is *sociology*, the study of the behavior of groups and masses of people. Here the same difficulties of measurement and control obtain as in psychology, but one has the feeling that the sociologists have set about developing a scientific approach in a more businesslike way than the psychologists. Sociology owes as much to the humanities as it does to science, yet its attempt to study and predict the behavior of groups and populations in a scientific manner is increasingly important in a world where so much is changing so fast as a result of advances in other scientific fields.

Those of you interested in psychology and sociology should bear in mind a basic difference between work in these fields and in other sciences. Even though they use certain laboratory methods, psychologists and sociologists are primarily working with *people*, not with instruments or chemical reactions. If you are a retiring sort of individual who looks forward to the quietness of the laboratory where you can work by yourself at your own pace, you will not be likely to fit into psychology or sociology very well. In these fields your work will throw you continuously in contact with people, sick and well, with whom you will be working and dealing. A liking and an appetite for social problems as well as scientific ones is probably the most important single qualification you could bring to work in these fields.

There are two other ways in which these sciences of behavior differ from other scientific fields, and in a way offer prospective workers a broader span of opportunity than other sciences.

Unlike most other sciences, training in psychology or sociology provides an excellent background for a number of completely nonscientific careers. In almost any kind of work that involves dealing with people—and more particularly, with influencing them—an understanding of psychology and sociology is of real tangible value. For teaching, for salesmanship, for politics, for hospital casework, and for a multitude of other kinds of work, college training in these fields is extremely useful.

These fields are also different in that advanced degrees may often be earned piecemeal, a year at a time; as we will see, advanced degrees in most sciences require a more concentrated period of "total effort."

But the basic scientific nature of these fields should not be sold short. We may live to see the day when sharply defined scientific principles of sociology and psychology will be desperately needed to save us from some of the dreadful consequences that advancement in other sciences may make possible.

This completes our admittedly brief and incomplete survey of training and opportunities in the major fields making up the circle of science. In each area, far more detailed information can be found, if you are interested in tracking it down. The libraries are full of books dealing with the lives and work of great scientists in the past, and a glance at any newspaper will reveal the avenues of progress being opened up by the great scientists of the future.

But there are certain other aspects of training in science which should at least be mentioned before closing our survey. A certain number of you will wish to carry your scientific training on for advanced degrees, a part of formal scientific training that has its own rewards and its own peculiar problems. All of you who enter scientific training in college will face certain decisions that will influence your educational program and your subsequent scientific career. In the next chapter we will consider some of the special problems you may encounter in your training, and express certain unpopular opinions which may nevertheless prove helpful as you go along the way.

NINE

Training in Science: Advice and Devices

WHEN I WAS IN MEDICAL SCHOOL, I earned a certain amount of my tuition money doing free lance editing for one of the major medical publishing houses in my spare time.

It was a rather frightening experience. It seemed that a certain scientist with a high professional standing and an enormous fund of experience in his work had written a textbook. The publisher wanted to publish this book but felt it needed a certain amount of editing before it was ready for the press. When I heard about the project over the telephone, it sounded like a lead-pipe cinch. Any idiot with a fundamental grasp of sentence structure could straighten out a couple of split infinitives, I told myself. . . .

Then I took a look at the manuscript, and saw what a slaughter of the King's English could really mean. On the first reading, I just couldn't understand it at all. Reading it again, I began to make sense out of parts of it, although whole paragraphs still appeared utterly unintelligible. It took half a dozen careful readings before I could really be sure what the man was trying to say. The content of the manuscript was excellent, the thinking and experience of a fine scientist. But the writing was illiterate.

Scientists have always been a little apologetic about their "illiteracy" in such nonscientific fields as basic English, the arts, history, and philosophy. Many scientists are, in fact, broadly educated and exceptionally literate people. But they are in the minority, and they do not just happen to be the way they are. Even though every effort seems to be made by the colleges and universities to instill something besides science into scientific students, the cards are stacked against it. Anyone starting in scientific training today stands an excellent chance of missing a whole vast and important segment of his education altogether unless he is alert to the threat of missing it, and recognizes why his nonscience training in college is at least as important as his science training.

The Nonscience in Scientific Training

As would-be scientists you may easily forget that when you begin your scientific training you are in fact entering a rigid specialty field, and leaving certain other things behind you. Once started, you face a great temptation to devote all of your time and energy to your specialty field, and simply ignore the other open doors in college—the humanities, history, philosophy, or the arts. Once you have completed your undergraduate training in science and have started graduate work, or found a position working in your field, your liberal education by and large is finished. From that point on, unless you are a most remarkable individual, you will eat, sleep, think, and live science. You will be in close association with people who are also eating, sleeping, thinking, and living science. You will be entering a tiny microcosm of life, and there will be nothing except your own curiosity and inclination to encourage you to look outside that microcosm even occasionally.

And the fact remains that no matter how brilliant a scientist you may be, no matter how immersed you are in your work, and no matter how wildly exciting you may find it, you are still first and foremost an intelligent human being who is a member of a community of human beings, and your contribution as a human being outweighs your contribution as a scientist.

When I think of the promising student who starts off to become a mathematician and drives through to his goal with little attention to anything else but math, I think of the tragedy of the prewar Japanese Olympic swimmers, young men whose swimming ability was discovered early and who were then trained intensively from childhood to swim the Olympic race and win it. This was their goal; nothing else mattered. At the age of twenty-one they came to the Olympic games, swam their races, often won them, and then disappeared like guttered-out candles.

No scientist can afford to restrict himself to a single narrow, machinelike function and ignore everything else around him. With the kind of work he does and the responsibility he bears, the scientist badly needs a broad background in the arts, in literature, in languages, and in human problems.

Even from the standpoint of sheer living comfort, this kind of a background is necessary. No one is quite so dull as the superintensified specialist who has no knowledge or interest in anything except his own superintensified specialty. It isn't hard to see why. Such a person has spent years learning what he knows about his specialty and still longer working on his own ideas in it. He will have to search far and wide for anyone who knows enough about his field of science and about his particular line of work to be able to talk to

him about it. If he wants to talk to anybody with less knowledge of his field—which he naturally considers the most
fascinating conversation topic in the world—he must first
be able to translate it into terms that someone else can
understand.

And chances are a thousand to one that he cannot do it.
He will have neither the patience nor the skill with language
necessary, and he will soon find that no one is making sense
out of what he is saying.

So as far as his field of work is concerned, the scientific
super-specialist too often lives in a world of his own that no
one else can enter. If his specialty is *all* that he knows, or is
interested in, he is going to be exceedingly dull company to
have around.

Worse yet, he is going to be a lonely individual himself.
The scientist who either ignores or fails to develop interests
in anything but his specialty field while he is training is
likely to lead a needlessly barren life.

You will have the opportunity during your undergraduate
college years to take a multitude of courses that have no
direct connection with science whatever. Some of these
courses are actually of immense practical value to the would-
be scientist, while others are valuable only in the doors they
will open to you for exploration. You will have opportunities
to investigate literature, history, music, dramatic arts, eco-
nomics, philosophy, psychology, or any one of a dozen other
pursuits. To willfully throw away these opportunities by de-
fault just doesn't make reasonable sense, yet there are thousands of prospective scientists who do just that—to their
lifelong regret.

Oddly enough, many science majors feel that they are
somehow selling their scientific training short by spending
time in nonscientific courses. They do not realize that they

are in fact selling themselves short if they don't. Such peccadilloes will never lure you away from your major interest in science, if that major interest is valid and deep-rooted; if other interests *will* lure you away, better to know it early and get out of scientific training then and there than to pretend that the other things are not there and end up feeling dissatisfied, cheated, and miserable in a field that you don't really like at all.

But of all the variety of nonscientific courses available to you in college, certain ones are as critically important to your training as the laboratory science courses are.

Any course which makes you work, which forces you to concentrate your efforts and trains you in disciplined thinking, is going to be of enormous help throughout your scientific career. Foreign languages provide such discipline and concentration. Unless you happen to have a natural-born, exceptional talent for languages, the study of foreign language will be hard work. It will require you to do steady day-by-day digging and studying, without much chance of relief, whether you happen to feel like it or not. If language study is inherently dull and distasteful to you, all the better; it will just require that much more discipline to force yourself to do a good job. And such an experience with relentless discipline in a course of study you dislike can be worth five hours of laboratory work every day of the week.

The reason is simple enough to see. Any scientist lives and works under a rigid discipline. The scientist is stuck with the job he selects to do. If there are parts of it that are tedious or dull or distasteful (and there always are), this is too bad—they still have to be done. This matter of concentrating your full attention and effort on a job which you do not basically care for is one of the toughest things in the world to do—yet the scientist is repeatedly forced to do it.

He may have to wade through weeks or months of utterly dreary reading and research before he has the background information he needs to dig into a problem that he is really excited about. He may have to scrub his own glassware, or pinch guinea pigs' tails, or do any number of things he would rather not do. . . .

But he does them just the same. All he needs is self-discipline.

Foreign languages have another very practical advantage to the scientist. Science is an international work. Every field of science has workers in a multitude of countries doing bits and pieces of the same job. Knowledge of a foreign language is helpful in following work in the journals, in studying or working abroad, or in personal contact with foreign scientists. Until quite recently, German was considered most useful as a second language for the scientist to read. It still is a highly useful scientific language, but odds are good that Russian will soon be considered the language of greatest importance. In any event, a sound reading and speaking background in some foreign language will inevitably be an advantage, as well as a useful kind of training in self-discipline and methods of study.

Curiously enough, certain aspects of philosophy can also be of a great deal of practical value to the would-be scientist. Successful work in science requires unclouded thinking, a knowledge of what constitutes proof, and a clear understanding of the difference between fact and inference. The scientist must be able to tell unsupported opinion and guesswork from proven fact, and needs to know how to establish the truth or falsehood of any given idea. Most basic college philosophy courses deal with the fundamentals of logic, argument, and proof; such courses are of considerable importance to anyone entering the world of science.

It may seem odd that anyone should need to learn how to argue. But a scientist is constantly involved in a rigid, formal kind of argument, considering unproven ideas, collecting evidence to support them, and then challenging the validity of the conclusions drawn from the evidence. You will very much need to know the difference between acceptable and unacceptable argument, between valid and fallacious logic. You will need to know the difference—and there is an enormous difference—between emotional, irrational argument and logical argument based on reason. How you may *feel* about a particular line of work you are doing has very little to do with whether that line of work is sound or unsound, or whether the conclusions you are drawing from it are true or untrue.

And the popular notion that the scientist is "unemotional" is true to this extent—that he dare not allow his feelings, his emotions, and enthusiasms to cloud his judgment, falsify his data or lead him astray in his experimental work. Every scientist must fight the temptation to try to fit the results of his experiments into the pattern that he wants them to fit into, whether they really fit or not. Some training in the philosophy of formal logic can be of great help in keeping you out of trouble with yourself and in avoiding the pitfalls of useless or misleading argument.

Finally, we come to the course requirement found in every qualified science-training curriculum in the country, a requirement dreaded by many and scorned by many more, a veritable "scientist's bane" of undergraduate college work— the required courses in English grammar and literature.

Although I have no statistics to support me, I suspect most college English professors would agree that of all students in college the science majors are the ones most likely to be bored, disinterested, or impatient with the basic English requirements laid down for them.

Just why this is so is a question I cannot answer. It seems to be almost traditional that scientists-in-training seek to shrug off their required courses in English as swiftly, and with as little work, as possible. There seems to be a feeling that proficiency in English grammar and composition is a skill far removed from science and useless to a scientist, yet I doubt if a prospective scientist could do himself a worse disservice by cutting off his own right hand than he does by deliberately short-changing his training in the use of basic English. The fact is that the vast majority of our scientists do not know the English language from Swahili, and their very illiteracy amounts to a twenty-five per cent handicap on their effectiveness as scientists in the work they are trying to do.

After all, the ability to communicate ideas is desperately important to any scientist. From the beginning of your scientific training on you will have to read and understand what you are reading. You will have such a huge volume of reading to do that you will need the ability to read rapidly and to grasp meanings swiftly and completely the first time around. In the course of your scientific training and work you will have to write reports of your work, discuss it in scientific meetings, and write descriptions of it for scientific journals. You may sooner or later find yourself writing textbooks and giving lectures. Certainly you are going to have to discuss your work on a technical level with other scientists, and on a nontechnical level with laymen.

Undoubtedly one of the major reasons for the misunderstanding of scientists and their work today is that the average scientist is poorly equipped to articulate and communicate to others what he is doing and what it means. When people complain that he is talking gibberish, they aren't exaggerating. That is exactly what he is talking, as far as they are concerned. In certain areas such as the medical sciences, this need for clear channels of communication is particularly great. A doctor's success in treating patients depends greatly on skillful use of language in order to gain the patients' understanding and forebearance. A disease like diabetes is difficult enough for the physician to understand, yet it is critical that the diabetic patient understand as much about his disease as possible. The patient will have trouble enough understanding it if the doctor can explain it to him in clear, simple, and lucid terms. He will be hopelessly lost if his physician is inarticulate or unable to express complex ideas in a simple fashion. Throughout the biological sciences we discover this need to express ideas clearly and simply so that anyone can understand them.

Basic command of English is the solution to the problem. As a scientist in training, you will have the choice of barely skimping through with the minimum investment you can make in English or really working to master it. Even if the idea seems unpalatable, I would strongly urge you to take the second alternative. You could not make a more important choice.

Advanced Degrees in Science

So far we have said very little about the steps in formal scientific training beyond college work for a bachelor's degree.

Of all the thousands of prospective scientists beginning their training, relatively few go on for advanced degrees. There are many reasons for this, a number of which have nothing to do with a student's intelligence or his interest in science.

In certain fields, such as medicine, an extensive period of graduate training is an absolute necessity. But in most scientific fields, as we have seen, there are excellent opportunities open to scientists without advanced training. The cost of four years of college alone is considerable. The scientist who wants to go on for a master's or a doctoral degree must make an additional investment in time and money—at least another year of training and probably two for a master's degree, and an additional three or four years for his doctorate. The majority of students feel the necessity to get out and make a living from their education after taking bachelor's degrees, and many promising doctorates in science are doubtless sacrificed simply on the basis of the time and funds they would require.

In fields other than science, advanced degrees can often be earned a bit at a time over a period of years. This kind of piecemeal work for advanced degrees in the sciences is not usually possible; the scientist who decides to take advanced training must usually find a way to continue his study in a concentrated full-time effort. At the same time he must have some means of supporting himself (and his family if he has one) during a time when his colleagues with lesser training are accepting choice, well-paying positions with security and promise for the future.

Of course, many colleges and universities offer *teaching fellowships* to graduate students. These are arrangements in which students working for advanced degrees receive a part of their tuition or living expenses or both in return for their services as instructors in the basic science courses, helping in recitation sections and student laboratory sessions at the same time that they are working toward their degrees. Almost any student who is determined to take an advanced degree and who has the ability to make the grade and the backing of his professors can find the means to limp along financially. Still, without other sources of income this sort of living is skimpy indeed; many students, particularly those who are married with young families, find that this kind of barely getting by wears thin after a while and allows no provisions for emergencies that may arise. They must carefully decide whether the length of time and the expense is going to be worth it to them in the long run.

For those of you who do decide to go the whole distance, there are certain things which are helpful to know. Not everyone who starts for a Ph.D. degree is necessarily going to succeed. There is no automatic guarantee that a degree will be forthcoming just because you have been accepted as a candidate. The student whose college grades have been poor and who has had little personal contact with his professors and instructors will have difficulty the moment he starts toward an advanced degree.

In fact, your success or failure in working for an advanced degree hangs a great deal more on personal judgments of your qualifications than on the results of examinations. From the beginning of advanced work you will be continuously judged on your natural ability, on your potential, on the way you approached your work, and on the whole question of whether you really have the makings of a creative scientist or not. This kind of judgment is necessarily very subjective, and sometimes unfair, but it is a system of granting advanced degrees which is established and accepted, and in the long run it makes surprisingly few bad choices.

The selection of a graduate school can present some problems. Many students proceed to take their master's or doctoral degrees at the school where they earned their undergraduate degrees, just because it seems easier to do so. This is not necessarily the wisest course to follow. For undergraduate work in science, almost any accredited college or university will offer acceptable training, but this is not so true of graduate work. When you are working in an advanced field on advanced problems, the quality of your professors, the example they set, the work they are doing, and their standing in their fields are important considerations. You would be wise to select your graduate school and your graduate professor with a great deal of care.

Certain schools are world-famous for their position in special scientific fields. In almost every case, the reputation of these schools arises from the reputation of the men making up their faculty and from the quality and importance of the work being done there. Just as a law degree from Harvard, or a medical degree from Johns Hopkins or the University of Pennsylvania will carry a prestige value over and above the value of the degree itself, certain schools have distinguished themselves in various scientific fields and confer special prestige to their graduate students. In these schools, graduate positions are eagerly sought out and difficult to obtain, but graduate degrees from such schools indicate a special quality of training. If you earn your degree at a top-rating school, no one will ever question your training. Anyone acquainted with science will know that your degree indeed represents what it is supposed to represent.

So you would do well to acquaint yourself with the schools that are doing the most exciting work and have the highest national reputation in your field of interest. In most fields, quite a selection is possible. In atomic physics, for example, California Institute of Technology and Massachusetts Institute of Technology are world famous, and there are a dozen other schools with enviable reputations in the field. In other fields there may be a single school that is the acknowledged leader, the guiding light in the field: Rutgers University, with its famous Institute of Microbiology, the "House that Waksman built," is not the only school offering advanced training in microbiology, but it is the one that has the finest reputation.

Of course, the famous science centers are not the only schools capable of offering excellent graduate training programs in the sciences. There are many that can offer students almost as much as the top-ranking ones in the various fields, and often a second factor of even greater importance than the school itself is better fulfilled at a less prominent school in a given field than in one of the great ones.

This second factor is the choice of your graduate professor. In undergraduate school, you are often lost in the throng. There may be dozens or even hundreds of students in your various lectures and laboratories, and your contact with the professors in the scientific departments is often superficial at best. The smaller recitation classes are usually conducted by instructors who are themselves graduate students teaching as part of their training programs.

But in working for a graduate degree you will be in much closer contact with your graduate professor. You will be one who has been selected from many, and whoever your professor is much of your future will lie in his hands. The quality of your training will depend in large part upon his ability, his interest in you, and his knowledge of his field. It will be with him that you plan your graduate program—the kind of work that you will do, the research that you are interested in, and the subject on which you will write your thesis. You will be in contact with him almost daily; he must be a man for whom you have profound respect, and who has respect for you.

Unfortunately, all professors of science in all schools do not command respect equally. Some are extremely learned men, exceptionally gifted in their fields, who simply cannot teach. Others are so deeply involved in the problems of their own work that their teaching and work with graduate students has become a chore that they tolerate only because they must, and they contribute as little interest and effort as possible. Some graduate professors cannot communicate with their students on any useful level at all; some are so interested in their own pet projects that they cannot take interest in projects that their students originate, and instead tend to encourage all of their students to become interested in the master's project and work as "satellite scientists" under his authority. Still others are so extremely jealous of their work and so afraid that someone will "steal" it from them that they are willing to contribute little or nothing of their knowledge to their graduate students.

Any of these men may be Nobel prize scientists, famous from one end of the world to the other—but they are poor choices for graduate professors.

And the fact is that at this level of scientific training your choice of graduate professor can strongly influence the type of scientist you will become and the career that you undertake. Throughout graduate training a close personal relationship grows up between the graduate professor and the student, a mutual respect, a mutual interest, and a mutual regard for each other's integrity as individuals. This sort of relationship can exert a lifelong influence; many graduate scientists have changed the whole course of their interest and work because of the powerful influence of a professor to whom they have become closely attached.

So you will certainly want to seek out a graduate professor whom you can like and admire as a person, as well as for his scientific stature—an individual whom you can approach on a personal level. It will be within his power to drive you out of your field in a long succession of frustrations, or to strike a spark of interest and excitement that will sustain you for the rest of your life. He should genuinely enjoy teaching and honestly be interested in the work you are doing. He should be able to talk to you and be willing to listen as well. He should like you as a person and feel a personal concern and responsibility for your progress or failure. All such ideals are not always fulfilled, but the closer you can approach them in your search for a graduate professor, the more likely you will meet with success in your graduate training.

Money and Marriage

Before closing our discussion of scientific education and the ways it is obtained, we should mention two problems which may well be on your mind at one time or another in the course of your training in science. Very possibly you will be wondering where marriage fits into the picture; and unless you are independently wealthy (may you be so lucky!) you will be wondering where the money for your training is going to come from.

The day when a young man felt that he had to be established in his work, with his education behind him, and a stable salary coming in before he could entertain thoughts of marriage is (happily, I might say) a time of the past. Today young people take a somewhat different view of marriage and the part each person plays in it. Modern girls are not enthusiastic about waiting until their men finish their education before marriage, particularly in the case of long-term scientific training. They would rather marry sooner, accept a period of thrifty living, and pitch in to help their husbands achieve their training. A great many students in scientific training today are marrying in the course of their college or postgraduate studies.

There is certainly much to be said for this "working together for a common goal" attitude, and there is a good deal of evidence to support the idea that married students do as good—if not better—work in their training as unmarried ones. When the veterans returning from World War II began college already married, there were long faces and sad wagging of heads; it was prophesied that these men could never carry the study load and still carry the responsibilities of marriage and family. Such worries were groundless, of course; married students in college and graduate school have done well, with the additional incentive to buckle down and get to work which many unmarried students do not have.

But a young man or woman interested in a career in science should recognize two things clearly before plunging into marriage while still in school.

First, it is going to mean a period of frugal living, perhaps for years. Two cannot live as cheaply as one, in spite of popular notions. The wife often can help out by working, but such plans can be knocked into a cocked hat very quickly when the first baby comes; the wife's providing while her husband studies is helpful indeed, but at best it can't be counted on for sure.

So anyone undertaking marriage while still in training runs a special risk: that he may have to terminate his scientific education earlier than he would wish in order to take a job that will provide for a family. For many prospective scientists this is perhaps not too bad an idea. Many would

be leaving school after their basic college training anyway
and most of those forced to change their original plans for
training would at least be carrying through for their bachelor's degrees.

But in a time when our need for trained graduate scientists with skill, imagination, and energy is very great, it
would be a tragedy for a young scientist with real potential
for advanced scientific work to be forced out of training by
the economic pressures of marriage. The loss would be great
to him, hamstringing him both in his ability to achieve what
he wants to achieve in science, and in his earning capacity
as a scientist. The loss is equally great to society, which loses
the contributions that he might make in a lifetime of advanced scientific work. The most unfortunate part is that
the student's real potential as a scientist doesn't even enter
into the picture. Too often he is simply forced to stop his
training because of financial conditions that are completely
out of his control and aggravated or brought to a head by
marriage. If you are planning marriage while you are in
school, it would be well to weigh this risk in your mind before taking the final step.

A second consideration is particularly difficult for one
who is hoping to be married during training, yet it is a
problem which should be recognized. It is a simple fact that
to some people the whole idea of science is an incomprehensible bore. For such people, marriage to someone engaged
in scientific work can be deadly. By the nature of his work
the scientist must be deeply immersed in his field and critically interested in it. He must contribute the majority of his
energy, time, and thinking to it, if he hopes to achieve anything worth while. A marriage partner should realize from
the beginning what she is bargaining for and recognize that
she will be sharing her mate with a discipline and an interest

with which she will have difficulty competing. A woman who can accept this state of affairs willingly and sympathetically can be an enormous help to her husband; one who resents it continually and never really accepts it can make life miserable for herself and her husband both. Anyone who is entering a scientific career should be very sure from the start that a prospective marriage partner knows what a scientific career is, and what its special requirements and demands will be in order to be as certain as is possible that this will not be the source of recurring conflict, as the marriage goes on.

The question of financing scientific training will come up to plague most would-be scientists at one time or another. In the early stages of training, supplementary work may be possible to help pay for tuition and living expenses. Students with science courses will usually have less time to spend in part-time work than those in other fields, but some outside work is often possible.

In advanced training, there is little if any opportunity for outside work, but here other resources, such as teaching fellowships and partial scholarships, become available. None of these programs provides a graduate student a handsome living—but at least they can provide enough to keep the wolf from the door if the student will settle for a slender budget. We have mentioned the annual science talent search, sponsored by Westinghouse, which provides generous scholarships for promising high school seniors entering scientific careers. The number of these scholarships offered is naturally limited, but the names of the winners and honorable mention are provided to colleges and universities all over the country. Students who do well in this contest often find other scholarship aid available.

In fact, as the critical importance of training top-level

scientists becomes more widely recognized, more and more money is becoming available to help subsidize deserving students with scientific promise. If you are eager for a career in science but have a problem with funds for training, don't hide your light under a bushel. Most colleges and universities have some scholarship funds available for undergraduate students; make your needs known if you have reason to think you have promise as a scientist. There is nothing dishonorable about accepting scholarship money, if you make an honest effort to do the best work you can while you are using it, nor is it dishonorable to borrow money from any source that will lend it to you. For the promising scientist, the end of a good training in science truly justifies almost any means of attaining it, short of bank robbery.

Graduate students often find help from the universities themselves, from industry, or from government grants. By and large, if a student has the potential to be a good scientist and is willing to buckle down and work, he will have little difficulty finding means to get through as long as he is willing to settle for slender living for a period of time.

The time has not yet come that *no* student with promise is lost to science because of lack of funds. But that time is not far off, because it is universally recognized today that the cost of training of scientists cannot begin to compare with the value of the work that their training will permit him to do.

TEN

The Future in Science

INEVITABLY, A BOOK OF THIS SORT will be somewhat disappointing for some of its readers.

To some extent, anyone reading a book about careers in science is looking for specific information applicable to himself and his own specific needs; he wouldn't be reading the book otherwise. As you have seen, much that we have had to say here has been general rather than specific. Admittedly we have left some gaping holes and have said very little in detail about specialty fields, costs of training, places to study, and so forth.

In some highly specialized fields like medicine or law such specific details are possible within the scope of a book of this sort. In discussing general scientific training, we simply have not had room for the details. Whole books could be written dealing with training and opportunities in physics alone, or in chemistry, or in the biological sciences, or in engineering, and I hope that such books will be written in the future on the background of this more general discussion.

But before we can think clearly about the specific details of a given scientific field, we need to know what science is, what a scientific life is like, and what the general patterns of scientific training in any field will be. In earlier chapters we have presented a picture of the world of science and of the place where various kinds of scientists fit into it. We have outlined in broad strokes the kind of training a scientist needs.

In surveying the whole world of science, we have talked a good deal about the exciting work and opportunities that exist for scientists today. Possibly we have talked too much. In our enthusiasm it is quite possible that we have overemphasized the exciting side of scientific work and underscored too heavily the importance of science and the role that scientists will play in the world of tomorrow.

Science is unquestionably important; nobody would argue that. But science is not the be-all and end-all of things. It is not the only kind of work and study which makes our world a better place to live in. There are even those scientists who wonder if scientists themselves have not done a good job of scrambling things up from time to time. It would be well to realize that the world we live in may ultimately be saved not by the scientists but by the poets, the humanists, and the philosophers. Certainly if we are to hope for peace among the people and nations of the world, it is not going to be achieved by science alone.

The critical factor is not so much the scientific knowledge we accumulate as the judgment, the wisdom, and the responsibility to use it properly. In a narrow sense, the scientist can work to discover the basic laws of nature, turn his knowledge over to the world, and then wash his hands of responsibility. After all, he could say, what the world does with his discoveries is no concern of his. But the fact remains that scientific knowledge can be violently dangerous if used unwisely or with poor judgment. No one in his right mind would give a loaded revolver to a five-year-old, yet science has provided us with the means of wiping every trace of life off the earth. Once the machinery is set in motion, it might never be stopped. And, unfortunately, no new knowledge of science will ever remove that threat.

But if science does not occupy the only important role in the world today, it is still changing the world and leading us into fields of study and knowledge never before dreamed of. So far we have mentioned only the well-established areas of scientific research, but we should not close without a few words about the areas just beyond the frontiers—the fringe areas into which science is slowly leading us. So far, these fringes are still the province of the science fiction writers, the speculators and the dreadful-story tellers. Tomorrow they could change our world and our lives in ways we would not think possible today—and there lies the fascination and the challenge of science in our time.

We continually search for power to run the machinery of our civilization. Already we have explored the atom as a source of power. So far we have only a hint of the dreadful, unimaginable power that lies trapped in our sun and in the other stars in the universe. It remains for the future scientists to learn how to harness that power so that men can use it without destroying themselves in the attempt.

Gravity is another force with enormous potential which has resisted all attempts to study it. Work being done on the control of gravitational forces and antigravity is still on the fringes of science, waiting for the breakthrough that will turn it into a powerful resource that man can use as he wishes.

Science has long been searching for an understanding of the human mind and how it behaves, and throughout history there have been reports of the curious "wild talents" which seem to appear from time to time in certain people under certain conditions. This kind of mysterious and unpredictable mental behavior is known as *extrasensory perception* or ESP. So far, few scientists are entirely certain that the phenomenon really exists, and its study today cannot be considered strictly "scientific." But within the next ten years this fascinating fringe of science may begin to come into focus, and such old science fiction standbys as levitation, telepathy, teleportation and telekinesis could well become the foundation of solid scientific study that could completely alter human relations, communication, and transportation.

Already atomic scientists have half convinced themselves of the theoretical existence of *contra-terrene matter*, subatomic particles carrying electrical charges directly opposite to those of normal or "terrene" atomic material. If it exists, CT matter would be completely and ultimately incompatible with the matter of which our known universe is composed, and there is endless room for speculation about the consequences of contact between terrene and contra-terrene matter—again, a possible source of unimaginable power or of universe-smashing destruction. There is just enough evidence that CT matter *could* exist to pique the curiosity of physicists around the world. The answer lies somewhere in the future, and the investigation could open up whole new fields of discovery that we have never even suspected before.

We have searched for cures for human illnesses since men first appeared on earth and have continuously sought means of extending our life expectancy. Now, at least, we can begin to see the major barriers that remain in our way. Future scientists will certainly see the length of useful human life extended, perhaps to hundreds of years—and science will also face the challenge of what to do with that longevity once it is achieved, and how to solve the problems of food supply and overpopulation that will follow in its wake.

We have searched for a better understanding of our own

solar system, and of the universe that lies beyond it. Today we are on the brink of the greatest adventure men have ever undertaken: the actual exploration of our solar system, and ultimately perhaps of the distant stars. Once again, the next generation of scientists will be the ones who pave the way, and we will live to see the first great steps taken.

And side by side with the study of the physical world that we can see is the tantalizing idea of the universes which may exist that we cannot see. We search for knowledge of the true nature of time and space, and we toy with the thought of parallel universes co-existent with our own, undetectable simply because we do not know how to cross from one to another. There are scientists who insist that travel through time or "sidewise in space" into coexisting universes is flatly impossible, that it would be violating the basic principles of conservation of energy and matter—yet even the most confirmed skeptics will admit that these basic principles may be only small parts of greater principles which we do not yet comprehend at all.

These are only a few of the fringes of science, work that lies waiting to be done once the groundwork is prepared. Some of these fringes will always be just fringes, fanciful ideas which will be thrown out as our understanding of the world of science grows. But scientists are the ones who will bring other fringe areas out of the realm of speculation. There will never be grounds for complaint that "everything important has already been done" in the world of science. Of one thing we can be certain: that there will be discovery and change, and this discovery and change will almost certainly occur at a far greater speed than we expect it to. The achievements of the last half century have so far outstripped the changes anticipated fifty years ago that it is laughable. Science builds upon itself, each new discovery speeding the rate of further discovery. There is no reason today to think that this acceleration will not continue.

On the contrary, there is every reason to believe that the growth of scientific knowledge in the last fifty years, vast as it has been, will appear insignificant in comparison to the growth that is to come in the next fifty years.

You who are starting toward careers in science today have a wonderful world of discovery ahead of you. You are entering the first stages of an Age of Exploration such as the world has never known before. The groundwork has been laid for you over the last two thousand years, and your legacy as a scientist today is rich indeed. It is an exciting time to be starting; if your heart and your imagination are here, you cannot possibly be disappointed.

INDEX

Advanced degrees in science, 163-168; choice of professor for, 166 f.; choice of school for, 165 f.

Aerodynamics, 39

Age of Exploration, 178

American Cancer Society, 142

American Cyanamid, 127

American Journal of Orthopedic Surgery, 25

American Telephone and Telegraph Co., 127

Anthropologist, 19, 147

Anthropology, 144

Applied science, 12; scientists, 52

Archaeologist, 147

Archaeology, 144

Astronomers, 26

Astronomy, 47, 144

Atom-smasher, 25

Atomic bomb, 53

Atomic energy, 128 f.

Bacteriology, 135

Basic research in industry, 89 f., 112 f.

Biochemistry, 48

Biological sciences, 130-143; opportunities in, 140-143. *See also* Life sciences

Biological scientists, challenges to, 142

Biology, 10, 23, 130-143. *See also* Biological sciences

Botanist, 133

Botany, 48. *See also* Biological sciences

"Bridge" sciences, 50. *See also* Psychology, Sociology

California Institute of Technology, 165

Cancer, 140

Careers in science, academic, 86; in industry, 88 ff.; in government, 87 f.; requirements for, 91-94

Chemistry, 10, 23, 39, 48; analytical, 121 f.; inorganic, 120 f.; opportunities in, 125-129; organic, 122; physical, 122 f.; undergraduate training in, 119-123

Chemists, new discoveries of, 126

Christian church, in relation to science, 46

Circle of science, 43; description of, 49 ff.

College, investment in, 11; minimum requirements in, 11; undergraduate training in, 69

College degree, requirements for, 58

Contra-terrene matter, 176

Cosmologist, 148

Cosmology, 149

Diabetes mellitus, 138; in relation to pregnancy, 138

Discipline, in thinking, 67; in science, 13, 67 f., 158 f.

179

DATE DUE

NOV 1 1 72			
MAY 5 1982			
GAYLORD			PRINTED IN U.S.A.